PRIMARY MATHEMATICS 3A

HOME INSTRUCTOR GUIDE

Authored by: Jennifer Hoerst

Avyx

Primary Mathematics 3A

Published by Avyx, Inc.
Reprinted 2009

Avyx, Inc.
8032 South Grant Way
Littleton, CO 80122-2705
USA

www.avyx.com
info@avyx.com
303-483-0140

ISBN 978-1-887840-98-9
Printed in the United States of America

Avyx, Inc., in an effort to help purchasers of the Singapore New Elementary Math 3A Textbook, is providing this Solutions Manual. For questions and support, please visit Singapore Math Inc. at www.singaporemath.com. There you can see a list of errors and their corrections, as well as contact information to submit additional errors or corrections.
NOTE: This site is not maintained by Avyx, Inc. This site is offered solely as a courtesy to support purchasers.

Preface

This guide is meant to help instructors using *Primary Mathematics 3A* when teaching one student or a small group of students. It should be used as a guide and adapted as needed. It contains

objectives,

notes to the instructor, providing added explanation of concepts,

instructional ideas and suggested activities,

and ideas for games

to reinforce concepts from the

corresponding textbook pages, learning tasks, and

"homework" assignments.

There are answers and solutions to all the learning tasks, workbook exercises and reviews, and textbook practices and reviews.

Included is a suggested weekly schedule and pages for mental math (in the appendix). The mental math pages are listed in the week the concept for that page is taught; they do not all need to be done that week and can be repeated. Practices and reviews in the text can be done as part of the lesson or independently by the student. Since some of the practice questions are challenging, they provide good opportunities for discussion. The mental math pages can be used as worksheets and many can also be done orally. They can be used any time after they are referenced in this guide, and can be used more than once for more practice.

Answers to the textbook practices and reviews and to the workbook exercises are given at the end of this guide. Answers to the learning tasks are given as they are encountered in the lessons. You can put paperclips on pages to keep track of where you are in each section.

This guide can be used with both the third edition and the U.S. edition of *Primary Mathematics 3A*.

3d› indicates portions pertaining only to the third edition, and

US› indicates portions pertaining only to the US edition (except for number words).

U.S. spellings and conventions will be used in this guide. Answers involving number words will use the current U.S. convention of reserving the word "and" for the decimal and not using it in number words for whole numbers. Revisions are called reviews in this guide.

Contents

Answers to Textbook Practices and Reviews

Week	Text Unit	Part	Textbook pages	Work book exercises	Additional Practice	Additional Material
1	1 Numbers to 1,000	1 Thousands, Hundreds, Tens and Ones	6-8	1		Mental Math 1, 2 Base-10 blocks Number discs Place value chart Dice
			9	2		
			10-11	3		
			12-13		Practice 1A, 1B	
		2 Number Patterns	14-16	4		
			17		Practice 1C	
					Vroot and Vroom 3 Game 1	
2	2 Addition and Subtraction	1 Sum and Difference	18-19	5		Number discs Place value chart Linking cubes
			20-21	6		
			21	7		
			22-23		Practice 2A, 2B	
					Vroot and Vroom 3, Game 2, Mission 3	
3		2 Adding Ones, Tens, Hundreds and Thousands	24-26	8	Mental Math 3, 4, 5	Number discs Place value chart Playing cards
			26	8a		
			27	9		
					Enrichment 1 Mental Math 6	
4		3 Subtracting Ones, Tens, Hundreds and Thousands	28-30	10	Mental Math 7	Number discs Place value chart Playing cards
			30-31	11	Mental Math 8	
			32-33	12		
			34-35		Practice 2C, 2D	
5		4 Two-Step Word Problems	36-37	13		Linking cubes Multiplication fact cards Number cards Dice
			38		Practice 2E	
				Rev. 1	Enrichment 2, 3 Mental Math 8, 9	
	3 Multiplication and Division	1 Looking Back	39-40	14-15	Mental Math 10, 11	
			40	16	Mental Math 12	
6			41	17	Mental Math 13	Linking cubes Fact cards
			42	18		
			43		Practice 3A	
		2 More Word Problems	44-46	19		
			46	20		
			47-48		Practice 3B, 3C	
				(28)	Vroot and Vroom 3 Problem Solving	

Week	Text Unit	Part	Textbook pages	Work book exercises	Additional Practice	Additional Material
7		3 Multiplying Ones, Tens and Hundreds	49-50	21	Mental Math 14	Base-10 blocks Number cards Place value chart
			50-51	22	Mental Math 15	
			51-52	23		
8			53	34		Base-10 blocks Hundred chart
			54-56		Practice 3D, 3E, 3F	
		4 Quotient and remainder	57-60	25		
				Rev. 2, 3	Enrichment 4	
9		5 Dividing Hundreds, Tens and Ones	61-63	26		Base-10 blocks Playing cards Dice Hundred chart
			64	27	Mental Math 16	
			65-67		Practice 3G, 3H	
					Review A	
10	4 Multiplication Tables of 6, 7, 8 and 9	1 Looking Back	69-69	(28)	Mental Math 17 Enrichment 5 Mental Math 18	Multiplication chart
11		2 Multiplying and Dividing by 6	70-73	29	Mental Math 19	Linking cubes Playing cards Dice Fact cards Timer Hundred chart
			73	30		
			74	31		
			74 75	32, 33	Practice 4A	
12		3 Multiplying and Dividing by 7	76-79	34	Mental Math 20	Linking cubes Playing cards Dice
			79	35		
			79	36-37		
			80-81	Rev. 4	Practice 4B, 4C	
13		4 Multiplying and Dividing by 8	82-83	38	Mental Math 21	Multiplication chart
			83	39		
			83	40-41		
			84-85		Practice 4D, 4E	

Week	Text Unit	Part	Textbook pages	Work book exercises	Additional Practice	Additional Material
14		5 Multiplying and Dividing by 9	86-88	42	Mental Math 22	Hundred chart Coins or counters Playing cards
			88	43		
			88	44-45		
			89		Practice 4F, 4G Mental Math 23, 24	
					Vroot and Vroom 3 Game 2, Mission 1	
15	5 Money	1 Dollars and Cents	91-92	46		Money
			93		Practice 5A	
		2 Addition	94-96	47		
			96-97	48		
16		3 Subtraction	98-100	49		Money
			100-101	50-51		
			102-103		Practice 5B, 5C Mental Math 24	
17			104	Rev. 5, 6	Review B	

Additional Material

Base-10 set.

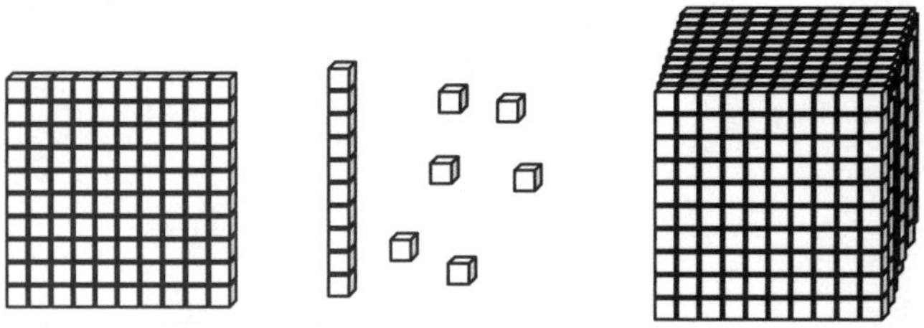

Number discs - Use plastic or cardboard discs and write "10,000" on one disc, "1000" on eighteen discs, "100" on eighteen discs, "10" on eighteen discs, and "1" on eighteen discs. If you have colored plastic counters, you can use one color for each place value.

Multilink cubes or other linking cubes or objects.

Place Value Chart
large enough to hold up to nine number discs each in the top and bottom halves.

Thousands	Hundreds	Tens	Ones

Hundred Chart
Make one or buy one with squares large enough to hold counters or coins.

1	2	3	4	5	6	7	8	9	10
11	12	13	14	15	16	17	18	19	20
21	22	23	24	25	26	27	28	29	30
31	32	33	34	35	36	37	38	39	40
41	42	43	44	45	46	47	48	49	50
51	52	53	54	55	56	57	58	59	60
61	62	63	64	65	66	67	68	69	70
71	72	73	74	75	76	77	78	79	80
81	82	83	84	85	86	87	88	89	90
91	92	93	94	95	96	97	98	99	100

Index cards for number cards and fact cards.

Playing cards

Dice

Money, play or real, coins and small bills.

Unit 1 Numbers to 10,000

Part 1 Thousands, Hundreds, Tens, and Ones

(1) Thousands (pp. 6-8)

Relate 4-digit numbers to thousands, hundreds, tens, and ones.
Read and write 4-digit numbers and corresponding number words.

In *Primary Mathematics 2A*, students learned to relate 3-digit numbers to the place value concept. This is extended here to 4 digit numbers.

➤ Use **base-10 blocks** and a **place value chart**. Have your student count out 9 ones onto the ones column. Ask her to add one more. She should remember that there can only be 9 ones. She must remove the ten ones and replace them with a ten in the tens column. Write the number 10. Remind her that the 0 is a place holder, showing that there are no ones. Have her count out 9 more tens. When she gets to the tenth ten, she must replace all the tens with a hundred. Write the number 100. Have her count out 9 more hundreds. Tell her that, as with the other place values, the hundreds place can only hold 9 hundreds. In order to add the tenth hundred, she must replace the ten hundreds with a 1000-cube. Write 1000. Remind her that this number is one thousand.

- How many ones are in ten? (10)
- How many tens are in one hundred? (10)
- How many hundreds are in one thousand? (10)
- If you had 2 such cubes, how many ones would there be? (two thousand)
- Write the number two thousand. (2,000 or 2000) We can put a comma to mark the thousand, but we don't have to. The comma makes it easier to read.
- Count by thousands to 9,000.
- One more thousand needs another place value. Write the number for ten thousand. (10,000). We put a comma in the number for every thousand for numbers that are 10,000 or more.
- How many thousands are in 10,000? (10)
- How many <u>ones</u> are in 1 (1)
- How many ones are in 10? (10)
- How many ones are in 100? (100)
- How many ones are in 1,000? (1,000)
- How many <u>tens</u> are in 10? (1)
- How many tens are in 100? (10)
- How many tens are in 1,000? (100)
- How many tens are in 10,000? (1,000)
- How many <u>hundreds</u> are in 100? (1)
- How many hundreds are in 1,000? (10)
- How many hundreds are in 3,000? (30)
- How many <u>tens</u> are in 7,000? (700)

➤ Use **number discs** and a **place value chart**. Show your student the number discs and relate them to the base-10 blocks. A disc with '1000' written on it represents one thousand, the same as a thousand cube. Place four 1000-discs on the chart. To find the number of hundreds, ask how many are in one of these thousands, then in the next thousand, etc. Lead them to see that there are ten in each thousand, and so 10 x 4 in 4 thousands.

- o How many <u>hundreds</u> are in 4000? (40)
- o How many <u>tens</u> are in 4000? (400)
- o How many <u>ones</u> are in 4000? (4000)

➤ Write some numbers and addition sentences and have your student place the corresponding number of discs on the chart. Include numbers where there are no hundreds, tens, or ones. Point out that in writing number words we use a comma after writing "thousand". Remind him that we use a dash between tens and ones, e.g. thirty-two.

8,092	eight thousand, ninety-two
4000 + 100 + 20 + 6	four thousand, one hundred twenty-six

Try some such as

90 + 4 + 2000 + 300	two thousand, three hundred ninety-four

Have him place the corresponding number of discs on the chart and read and write the number and the number words.

Page 6-7 and Learning Tasks 1-2, p. 8

(a) 349 (b) 2435
(c) five thousand, nine hundred ninety-eight;
six thousand, twelve

1. (a) 3274
2. (a) 2045 (b) 1307 (c) 4250

Workbook Exercise 1

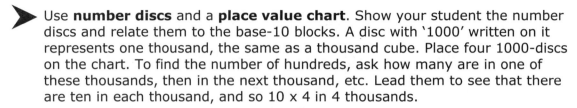

(2) Place Value (p. 9)

Relate each digit in a 4-digit number to its place value.

Write the numbers 1, 2, 3 and 4. Ask your student how he would find out how many 4-digit numbers he can make from these numbers. Help him to discover a systematic way of listing them. You can show them a tree diagram to keep track of the possibilities.

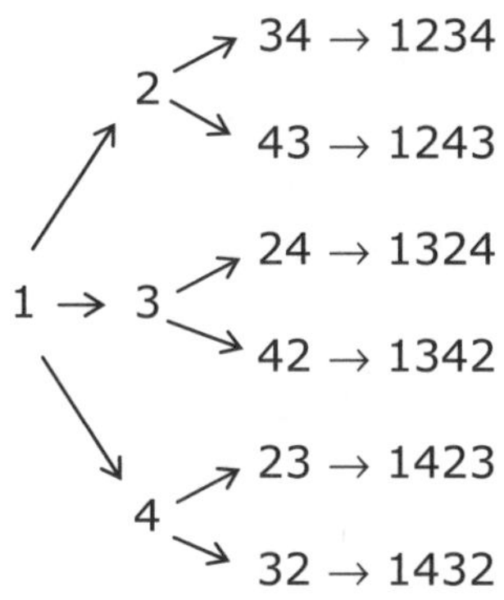

There are 6 possible 4-digit numbers for each different starting number (thousand), and 6 x 4 = 24 different 4-digit numbers (4 x 3 x 2 x 1 possibilities). Write down all the possibilities.

Point to the digits of some of the numbers and ask what the digit stands for. For example, point to the 4 in 1423. The 4 stands for 400. Then point to the 4 in 4123. The 4 stands for 4,000.

Point to some of the numbers and ask for the digit in a certain place value. For example, point to 1234 and ask for the digit in the tens place.

Ask for the number that has a digit in a certain place. For example, ask for the number that has 3 in the hundreds place.

Learning Tasks 3-6, p. 9

3. The digit 8 stands for 800
   The digit 4 stands for 4
4. (a) 500 (b) 5,000 (c) 50
5. 4; 400 3; 3,000
6. 8 - 8,000 1 - 100 3 - 30 7 - 7

Workbook Exercise 2

(3) Comparing 4-Digit Numbers (pp. 10-11)

Compare and order 4-digit numbers.

Students learned to compare and order 3-digit numbers in Primary Mathematics 2. Here the concepts are extended to 4-digit numbers.

Write some 4-digit numbers on **index cards** or pieces of paper, such as 4325, 3562, 3462, 3458, 3457, 4332. Your student must put them in order. Remind her that she must compare the digits in the highest place value first, then in the next highest place value, and so on. Illustrate with number discs.

- The smallest 4-digit number comes just after what number? (999)
- The largest 4-digit number comes just before what number? (10,000)
- Find a 4-digit number where none of the digits is 0, the sum of all the digits is 15, the hundreds digit is twice the tens digit, and the tens digit is three times the ones digit. (5631)

Roll the Thousands

Material: **Number cube or die**, paper and pencil for each player.

Procedure: Write four dashes on the paper for each place value. Each player rolls a die four times. After each roll, the player must decide whether to write the number rolled in the hundreds place, the tens place, or the ones place. Once written it must remain in that place. The players hide their numbers from each other until all players have rolled and written their number. The player with the highest number wins.

Learning Tasks 7-14, pp. 10-11
Illustrate these problems with number discs if necessary.

	7.	(a) 4316; 5264		(b) 2325; 2352
US➤	8.	(a) less	(b) less	(c) greater
3d➤	8.	(a) smaller	(b) smaller	(c) greater
	9.	5073	4973	
	10.	1000	9999	
	11.	4123, 3412, 3142, 2431		
	12.	913, 1703, 1892, 9003		
	13.	540	405	
	14.	(a) 8720	(b) 3479	

Workbook Exercise 3

Part 2 Number Patterns

(1) Number Patterns (pp. 14-16)

Add and subtract 1, 10, 100, or 1,000 to or from a number less than 10,000.

In this section, the student must focus on the place value of the digit.

Use **number discs** and a **place-value chart**. Place a 4-digit number on the chart. Write the number. Ask your student to give the number that is 1 more or 1 less, 10 more or 10 less, 100 more or 100 less, 1,000 more or 1,000 less than the number on the chart, adding the corresponding number disc and writing the given number. Do numbers where only the digit in one place is changed. For example:

- What number is 10 more than the new number 4575? (4585)
- What number is 100 more than 4585? (4685)
- What number is 1,000 more than 4685? (5685)
- What number is 1 less than 5685? (5684)
- What number is 100 less than 5684? (5584)

Repeat without the number discs and place value chart. Write the equations.

For example:

4567 + 100 = ?
8912 − 1000 = ?

Have your student practice counting out loud by tens, hundreds, or thousands.

Page 14 and Learning Tasks 1-2, p. 15

6442 is 100 more than 6342
6542 is 100 more than 6442
6542
6642
(a) 6642; 6742
(b) 9342; 10,342
(c) 6345; 6346
(d) 6372; 6382

1. (a) 3724 (b) 3625 (c) 3634 (d) 4624
2. (a) 4732 (b) 5731 (c) 5722 (d) 5632

➤ Use **number discs** and a **place-value chart**. Repeat the activity above but do problems where regrouping is necessary. For example:

What is 1 less than 3900? (3899)
What number is 10 more than 3899? (3909)
What number is 100 more than 3909? (4009)

➤ Write two 4 digit numbers on the board. Have your student count from one to the other, both forward and backward, first by thousands, then by hundreds, then by tens, then by ones. She should notice that when adding the next thousand, hundred, or ten will make the number too high she must switch to counting by the next lower place value.
For example, if the two numbers are 5648 and 8273:

Forward: **5**648, **6**648, **7**648, 7**7**48, 7**8**48, 7**9**48, **80**48, 8**1**48, 8**2**48, 82**5**8, 82**6**8, 826**9**, 82**70**, 827**1**, 827**2**, 827**3**

Backward: **8**273, **7**273, **6**273, 6**1**73, 6**0**73, **59**73, 5**8**73, 5**7**73, 5**6**73, 56**6**3, 56**5**3, 565**2**, 565**1**, 565**0**, 56**49**, 56**48**

➤ Write some patterns for your student. The tens, hundreds, or thousands should increase or decrease by 1 or 2. For extra challenge try some where the digits in two places increase or decrease, or where they increase in one place and decrease in the other. Your student has to look at the digits in each place to see the pattern, rather than determining the sequence by finding the difference between successive terms. For example:

4123, 5123, 6123, ____ (thousands increase by 1)

3932, 3832, 3732, ____ (hundreds decrease by 1)

4512, 4532, 4552, ____ (tens increase by 2)

3492, 4392, 5292, ____ (thousands increase by 1, hundreds decrease by 1)

Learning Tasks 3-4, p. 16

3. (a) 1708, 1718
   (b) 1978, 2078
   (c) 4678, 5678, 6678, 7678

4. (a) 3100 (b) 3128 (c) 4098
   (d) 3298 (e) 8893 (f) 8093

Workbook Exercise 4

Unit 2 Addition and Subtraction

Part 1 Sum and Difference

(1) Sum and Difference (pp. 18-19)

Understand the terms **sum** and **difference**.
Represent mathematical statements with pictorial models.
Learn to use part-whole and comparison models.

In Primary Mathematics 1 and 2, students learned to relate addition and subtraction to the part-whole concept, and to use subtraction to compare two sets of objects to find out how many more or less objects one set had than the other. However, the terms **sum** and **difference** were not formally introduced. These terms are introduced here through pictorial models. These models will be used to help the students solve word problems. There are two types of models being introduced here, a part-whole model using one bar, and a comparison model using two or more bars to represent the quantities.

Modeling is a tool used to solve problems. The ability to draw models will be useful later in translating word problems into algebraic equations. In algebra, an unknown is represented by a variable, such as x. In modeling, an unknown bar length can be considered similar to a variable, though problems solved using modeling in Primary Mathematics 3-6 are often solved differently than they would be when setting up an algebraic equation since it is usually the smallest quantity that is used as the unit, or unknown. However, a concrete, pictorial foundation will greatly facilitate the understanding of algebraic representations later. Use discretion when requiring your student to model workbook exercises. Encourage her to draw models so that she becomes familiar with modeling and can use it to solve problems when necessary, but do not insist that she draw models in the workbook exercises if she can easily solve the problem without a model. Some students can visualize the model mentally.

Remind your students that to find a whole given two parts, we add. Draw the number bond and the equation.

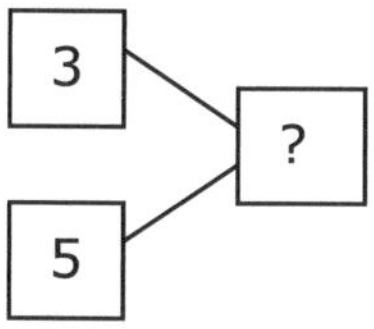

3 + 5 = ?

Explain that when we add two numbers, we are finding their **sum**.

Ask for the **sum** of a few addition problems. For example:

What is the sum of 4 and 6?
What is the sum of 402 and 123?

Use **linking cubes**, base-10 unit cubes, or legos. Set out 3 of one color, 5 of another, and 8 of a third color. Line them up.

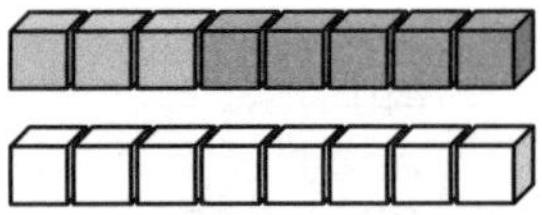

Show how this can be represented by drawing bars:

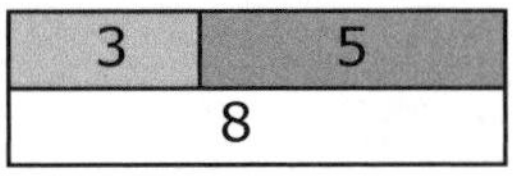

Explain that a bar representing a larger value should be drawn so that it looks longer than a bar representing a smaller value.

Ask your student to show with bars the **sum** of 432 and 104. One should be quite a bit smaller than the other:

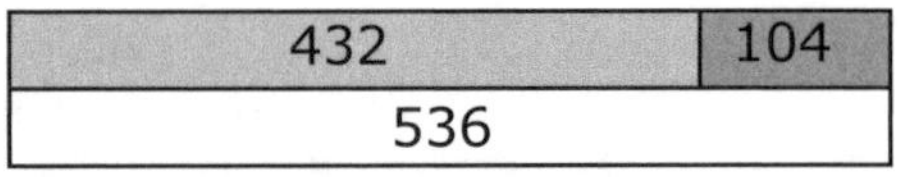

Tell him that as numbers become bigger and problems more interesting, it is easier to put numbers outside the bars so that the bars can be "cut up" later, like when they will be used to show division or fractions. In this part-whole model, the bar representing the whole does not have to be drawn separately

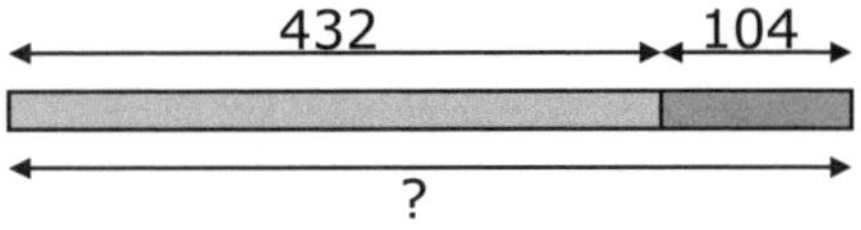

Draw the number bond again, this time showing a missing part. Write the equation. Remind your student that to find a missing part given the whole and one part, we subtract:

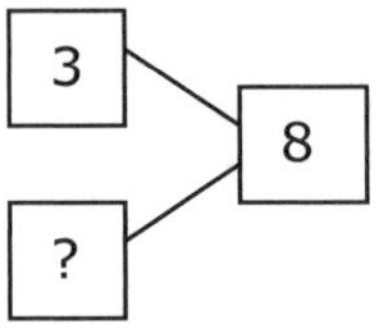

8 – 3 = ?

Show him a model for this:

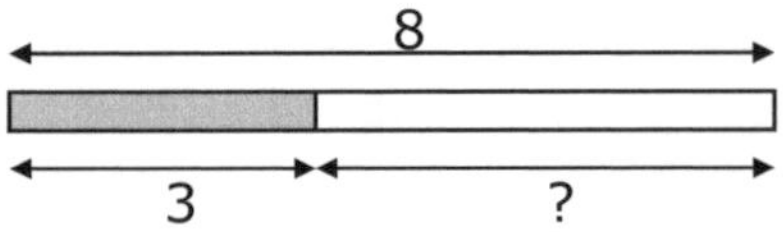

Ask him to draw a model to help him find the number that is 62 less than 104.

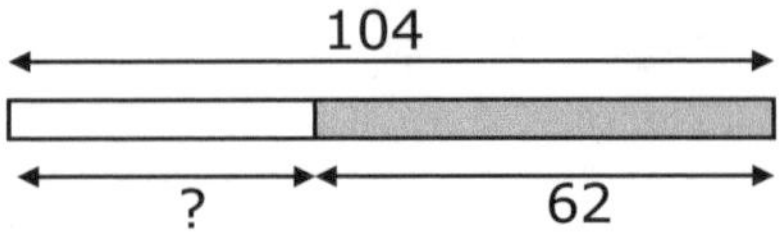

Point out that it is easy to see from the model that he needs to subtract to find the answer. Models can be used to help decide whether to add or subtract to find the answer to a problem.

Use the **linking cubes**. Remind your student that we can find how many **more** objects we have in one set than another by subtraction. 8 is how many **more** than 3? Or, 3 is how many **less** than 8?

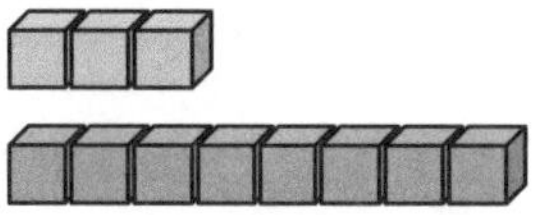

Tell him we are finding the **difference** between 8 and 5. Ask for the difference in a few problems. For example:

What is the difference between 4 and 6? (2)
What is the difference between 452 and 123? (329)

In this case, we are **comparing** two numbers. Illustrate with a model. We use bars to show the amounts and we put them one on top of the other to compare them. The left edges should line up, and the larger number should be drawn with a longer bar.

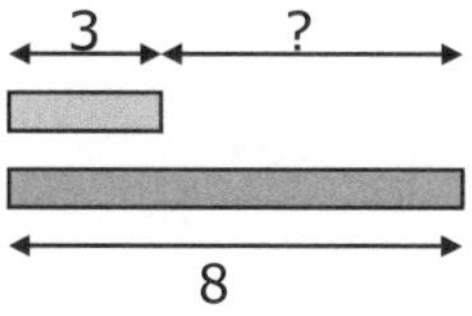

Ask him to model the difference between 620 and 510. Help him determine a reasonable length for the two numbers. Note that one number is close to the size of the other, so the two bars should be close to the same size. (Do not worry about having exact relative proportions.)

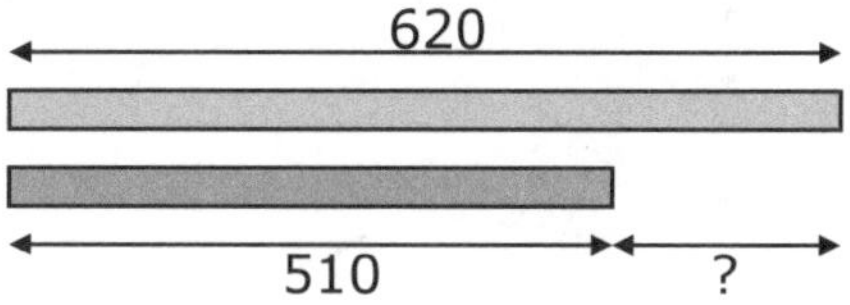

Page 18 and Learning Tasks 1-3, p. 19
Have your student model learning task 3. Use a part-whole model for 3.(a) and 3.(b) and a comparison model for 3.(c) and 3.(d).

(a) 11; 11 (b) 3; 3

1. (a) 13; 13 (b) 3; 3
2. (a) 90 + 54 = **144** (b) 90 − 54 = **36**
3. (a)

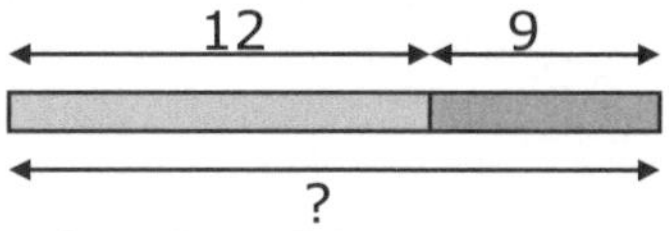

12 + 9 = **21**

(b)

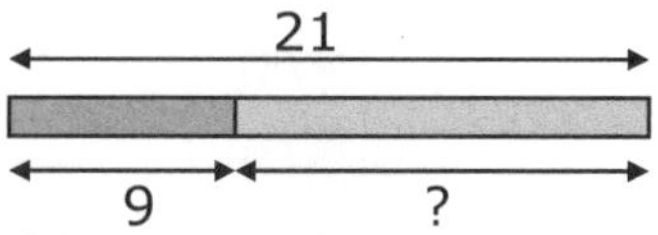

21 − 9 = **12**

(c)

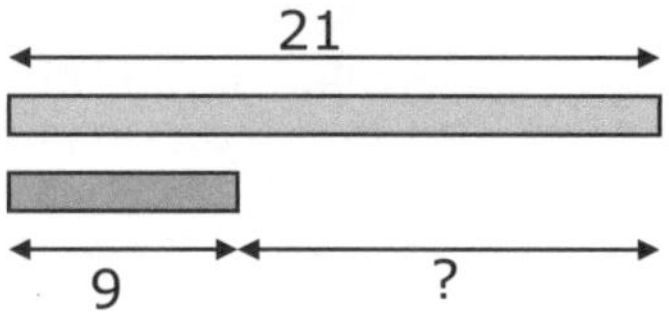

21 − 9 = **12**

(d)

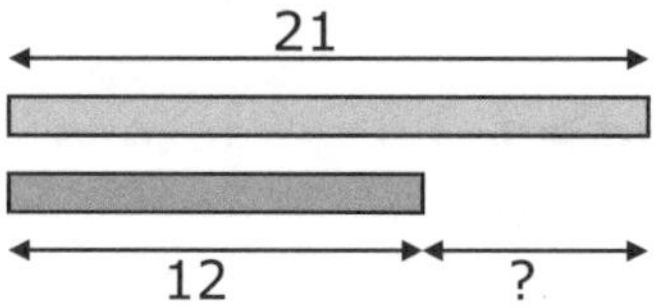

21 − 12 = **9**

Workbook Exercise 5

(2) One-Step Word Problems (pp. 20-21)

Use concrete models to solve one-step word problems.

Learning Tasks 4-7, pp. 20-21

As you go through these, ask your student pertinent questions so that he look at each bit of information given in the problem, such as:

What do we need to find?
What information are we given?
Are we given a total? What part is given?
Are we given two parts? Which part is larger?
Are we comparing two amounts? What two? Which is larger?

Ask him to identify which part of the model represents which piece of information from the problem. For example, in exercise 5, ask what the dark pink bar represents and what the light pink bar represents.

4. 388
5. 316
6. 15
7. 121

Workbook Exercise 6

(3) Introduction to Two-Step Word Problems (p. 21)

Use concrete models to solve word problems with two steps.

Learning Task 8 is an introduction to two-step word problems, which will be taught in part 4 of this unit. Both steps are given as (a) and (b)

Learning Task 8, p. 21

Since we are given how many less pages are read in the afternoon than in the morning, the number of pages read in the morning is being compared to the number of pages read in the afternoon, so we can draw a comparison model. The top bar is the number of pages read in the morning. Encourage your student to label the bars with what they represent – in this case he could use "m" for morning and "a" for afternoon, or "a.m." and "p.m."

The solution to (b) can be found from the given model, but the model can also be redrawn as a part-whole model if necessary.

➤ Give your student additional problems to practice drawing models. Discuss approaches to more challenging problems so she can see a benefit to drawing models. For example:

12 less than 48 is ______.

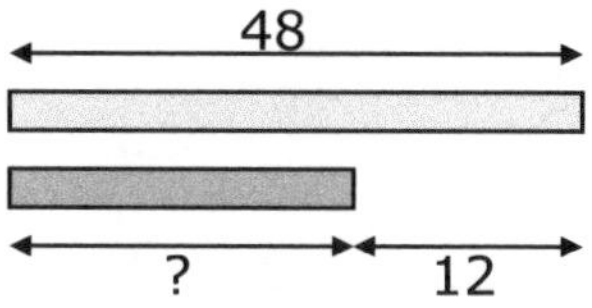

48 − 12 = **36**

18 more than ________ is 96.

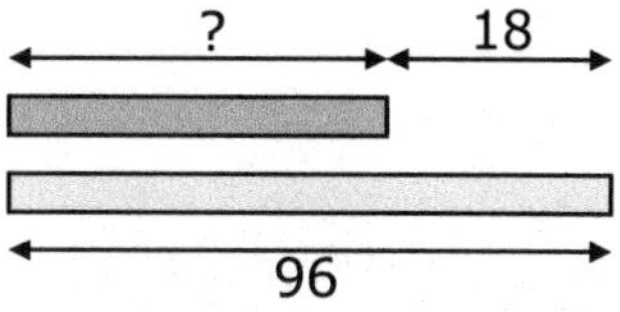

96 − 18 = **78**

______ less than 78 is 51.

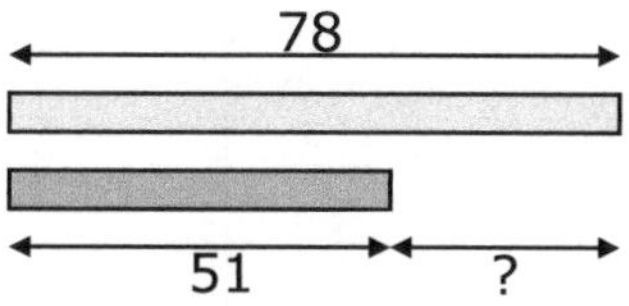

78 − 51 = **27**

Find the number that is 159 greater than 687.

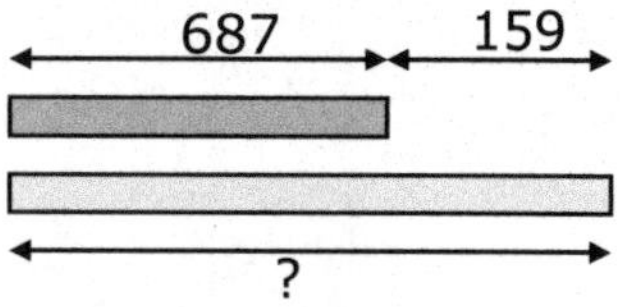

687 + 159 = **846**

Paul gave $134 to John and had $56 left. How much money did Paul have at first?

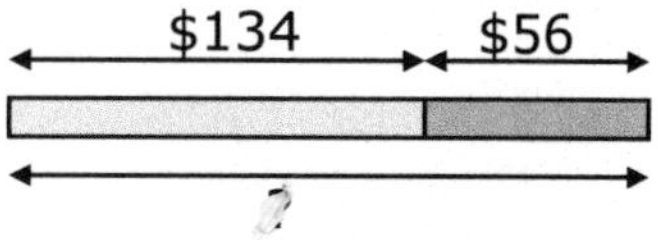

$134 + $56 = **$190**

Mary had 120 more stamps than Jill. Jill had 68 stamps.

(a) How many stamps did Mary have?
68 + 120 = **188**

(b) How many stamps did the two girls have?
188 + 68 = **256**

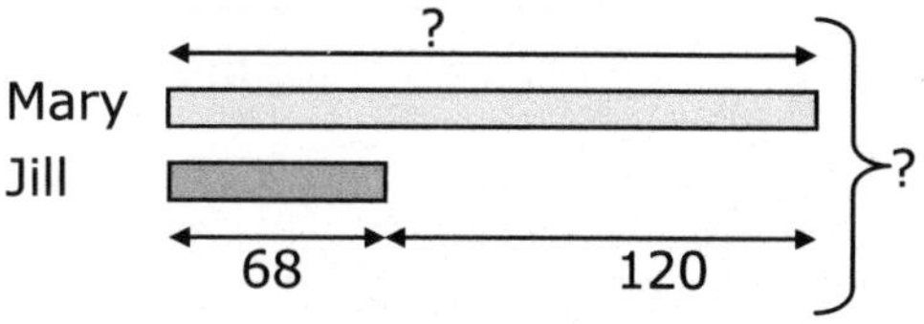

Daniel and Peter have 450 marbles. Daniel has 248 marbles.

(a) How many marbles does Peter have?
450 − 248 = **202**

(b) Who has more marbles? How much more?
Daniel.
248 − 202 = **46**

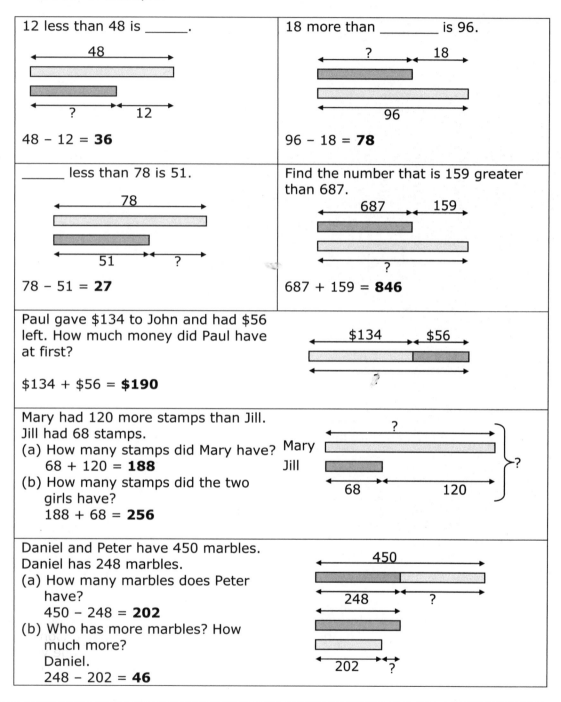

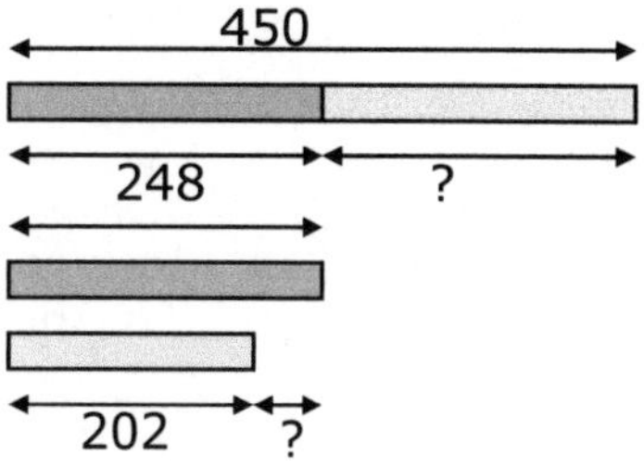

Workbook Exercise 7

Part 2 Adding Ones, Tens, Hundreds and Thousands

In Primary Mathematics 2, the student learned how to add numbers under 1,000 with renaming, using the standard algorithm. This concept is extended in this section to numbers under 10,000. The student should be familiar with the procedure and may not have much difficulty in extending it here. Illustrate as many problems as necessary, one step at a time, with base-10 material, such as the number discs, writing each step down as you proceed so that the student sees the connection between the concrete manipulatives and the numerical representation of each step. Allow your student to have access to the manipulatives when doing the problems. A general procedure is given here.

Place the discs on the place value chart. Trade in ten ones for a ten and put it in the tens column.

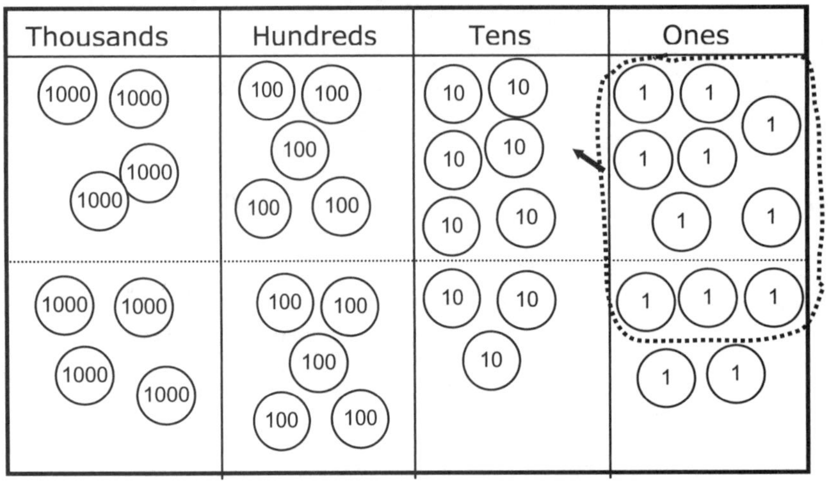

Write the problem:

$$\begin{array}{r} 4\,5\,6\,7 \\ +\,4\,5\,3\,5 \\ \hline \end{array}$$

Add the ones (12). Rename 10 ones as a ten and write it above the tens. Write the total ones left (2) below the line in the ones place.

$$\begin{array}{r} 1\;\; \\ 4\,5\,6\,7 \\ +\,4\,5\,3\,5 \\ \hline 2 \end{array}$$

Trade in 10 tens for a hundred and put it in the hundreds column.

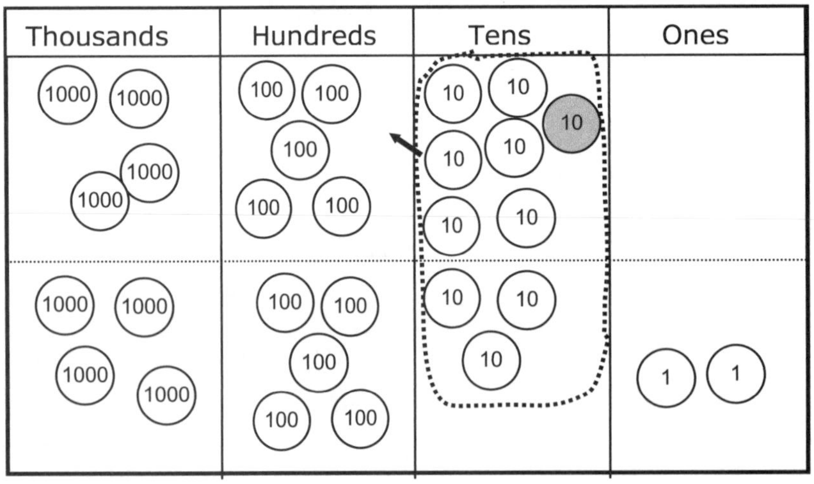

Add the tens. (10) Rename them as a hundred and write 1 above the hundreds. Write the total number of tens (0) below the line in the tens place.

$$\begin{array}{r} 1\,1\;\; \\ 4\,5\,6\,7 \\ +\,4\,5\,3\,5 \\ \hline 0\,2 \end{array}$$

Trade in 10 hundreds for a thousand and put it in the thousands column.

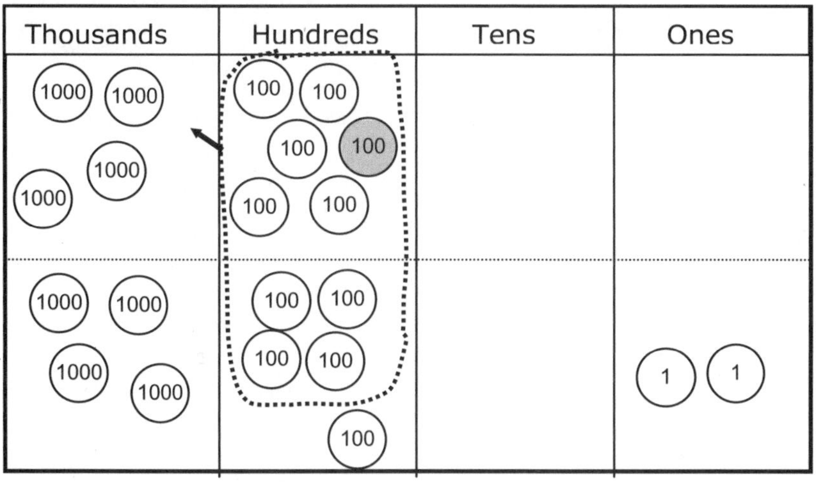

Add the hundreds. (11) Rename 10 hundreds as a thousand and write a 1 above the thousands. Write the total number of hundreds left below the line in the hundreds place.

$$\begin{array}{r} {\scriptstyle 1\ 1\ 1\ \ } \\ 4\ 5\ 6\ 7 \\ +\,4\ 5\ 3\ 5 \\ \hline 1\ 0\ 2 \end{array}$$

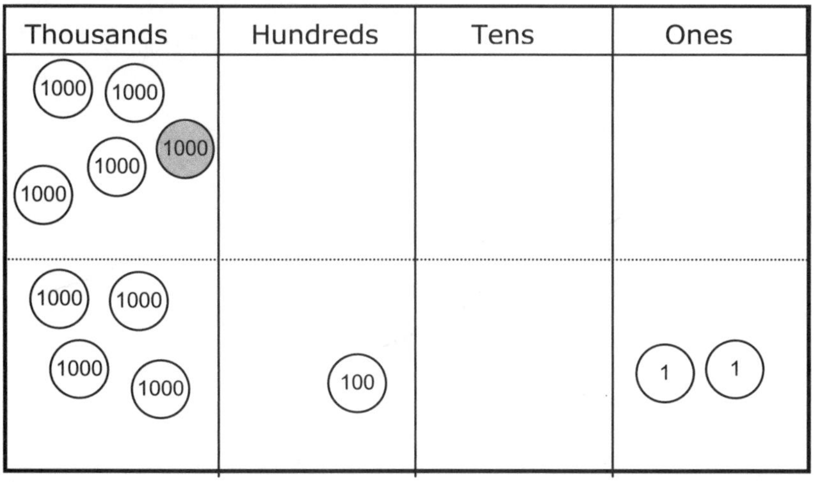

Add the thousands and write the sum below the line in the thousands place.

$$\begin{array}{r} {\scriptstyle 1\ 1\ 1\ \ } \\ 4\ 5\ 6\ 7 \\ +\,4\ 5\ 3\ 5 \\ \hline 9\ 1\ 0\ 2 \end{array}$$

(1) Renaming Ones, Tens, or Hundreds (pp. 24-26)

Add 4-digit numbers where the ones, tens, or hundreds are renamed.

Trade-In

Material: **Number discs**, **place value chart**, and **playing cards** with the face cards removed and tens made into 0 (by whiting out the 1 and the 10 items) or four sets of number cards 0 to 9.

Procedure: Single player: Place a one on the chart. Draw a card. The number drawn shows the number of ones to add to the chart. Trade in ones for a ten if necessary. Draw another card. The number drawn is the number of tens to add. Trade in tens for a hundred if necessary. Draw a third time, and add hundreds, trading in if necessary. Draw three more cards one after the other, each time adding ones, tens, or hundreds in that order. Continue until a specified target number of thousands is reached.

Page 24

Discuss, using and moving actual number discs.

Learning Tasks 1-5, pp. 25-26

In learning task 1, there is no renaming. They may be rewritten vertically, but your student may be able to keep track of the place values of each digit without rewriting. In learning task 5, there is one renaming. Rewrite the problems vertically. Illustrate with number discs if necessary.

1. (a) 4268 (b) 4283
   (c) 4663 (d) 7263
   (e) 4688 (f) 7688
2. 2050
3. 5900
4. 4000
5. (a) 1262 (b) 3654
   (c) 4839 (d) 7542
   (e) 7197 (f) 8362

Trade-In (variation)

See directions for Trade-In above. The student writes the addition problems down as the game is played, rather than using number discs.

Multi-player: Players take turns drawing a card. The first one to reach a target number wins.

Workbook Exercise 8
Problem 1 does not involve renaming. It is not necessary to rewrite these vertically unless the student needs to. Your student must pay attention to the place value of each digit.

(2) Renaming Twice (p. 26)

Add 4-digit numbers where renaming occurs twice.

Learning Tasks 6-7, p. 26
Illustrate these with number discs, if necessary.

7. (a) 1520 (b) 8920
   (c) 6258 (d) 8037
   (e) 8091 (f) 7382

Palindromes
Explain to your student that palindromes are words or phrases that read the same backwards and forwards. For example:

mom

Was it a bar or a bat I saw?

Palindromes can also be numbers that read the same backwards and forwards. For example, 454 and 8338 are palindromes.

If you take any 2-digit or greater number and add the digits of the number to the digits in reverse order and continue this process with each successive sum, you eventually get a numerical palindrome. Let your student try it with some 2- or 3-digit numbers:

$$\begin{array}{r} 28 \\ +\ 82 \\ \hline 110 \\ +\ 011 \\ \hline 121 \end{array} \qquad \begin{array}{r} 283 \\ +\ 382 \\ \hline 665 \\ +\ 566 \\ \hline 1231 \\ +\ 1321 \\ \hline 2552 \end{array} \qquad \begin{array}{r} 681 \\ +\ 186 \\ \hline 867 \\ +\ 768 \\ \hline 1635 \\ +\ 5361 \\ \hline 6996 \end{array}$$

Exercise 8a (In the appendix of this guide)

(3) Renaming Three Times (p. 27)

Add 4-digit numbers where renaming occurs three times.

Learning Tasks 8-9, p. 27
Illustrate with number discs, if necessary.

9. (a) 6013 (b) 7400
   (c) 8800 (d) 5400

The Smallest Number

Material: **Playing cards** with the face cards and tens removed.

Procedure: Shuffle cards and deal 8 cards to each player. Aces are ones. Each player must arrange the cards into two 4-digit numbers such that the sum gives the smallest number possible. The player with the smallest sum wins.

Workbook Exercise 9

Enrichment 1 – Mental Math

In Primary Mathematics 1 and 2, the student learned to mentally add numbers with one regrouping in ones, such as

$45 + 8$

The student can do this either as

$45 + 8 = 40 + 5 + 8 = 40 + 13 = 40 + 10 + 3 = 53$

Or as

$45 + 8 = 40 + 5 + 8 = 40 + 3 + 2 + 8 = 40 + 10 + 3 = 53$
("making a ten" with the 8)

In either case, before writing down the tens, we can "look ahead" to see if there will be one more ten. In

$345 + 8$

we can first write down the hundreds (3), and then add 45 + 8 as above, writing down the tens first and then the ones.

We can now mentally add 4-digit and 1-digit numbers, such as

$2345 + 8 = 2353$

by writing down first the thousands, then the hundreds, then "looking ahead" before writing down the tens.

This "mental regrouping" has also been done with tens, such as

$450 + 80 = 530$

Here, we can think 45 tens + 8 tens, and add the same way as adding ones above, and then writing a 0 for ones.

The student also learned to mentally add

$452 + 80 = 532$

by adding tens as above (450 + 80) then writing down the ones. This can be extended to hundreds:

$4500 + 800 = 5300$

Here, regrouping occurs only in the hundreds, and we can "look ahead" before writing down the thousands to see if adding the hundreds will increase the thousands by 1. This procedure can also be followed in

$4500 + 802 = 5302$

We can add 4500 and 800, and write down 53, then 0 for no tens, then 2 for ones. In

$4512 + 842 = 5354$

we can first add 4500 and 800 to get 5300, write down 53, and then add the tens and then the ones:

$4512 + 842 = 4500 + 800 + 12 + 42 = 5354$

These types of problems are given in Mental Math 6. Help your student work through them.

Part 3 Subtracting Ones, Tens, Hundreds and Thousands

In Primary Mathematics 2, the student learned how to subtract numbers under 1,000 with renaming, using the standard algorithm. This concept is extended in this section to numbers under 10,000. The student should be familiar with the procedure and may not have much difficulty in extending it here. Illustrate as many problems as necessary, one step at a time, with base-10 material, such as the number discs, writing each step down as you proceed so that the student sees the connection between the concrete manipulatives and the numerical representation of each step. Allow your student to have access to the manipulatives when doing the problems. A general procedure is given here.

Place the discs on the place value chart. There are not enough ones to take away 9, so rename a ten for 10 ones.

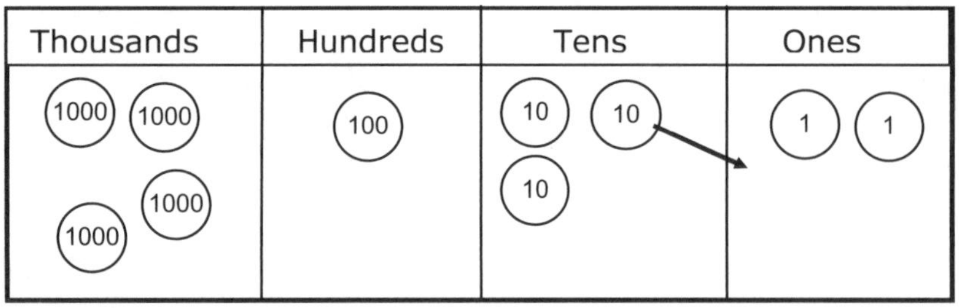

Remove 9 ones.

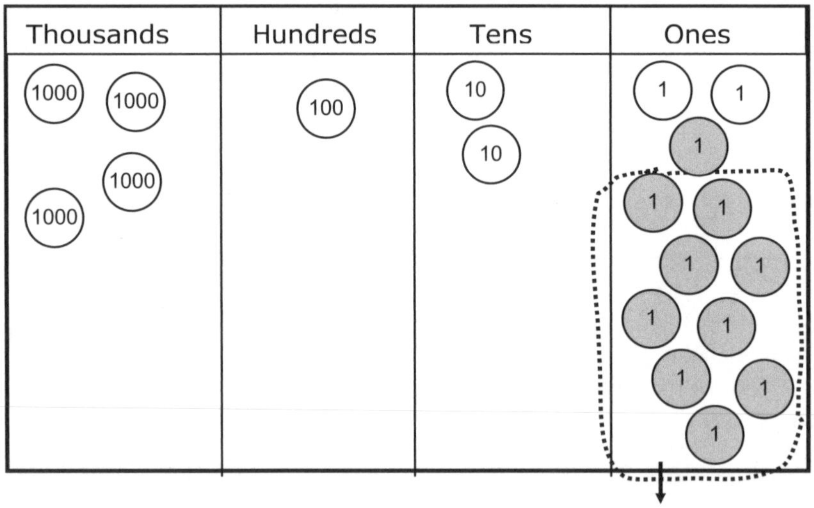

Write the problem:

$$\begin{array}{r} 4\ 1\ 3\ 2 \\ -\ 1\ 6\ 7\ 9 \\ \hline \end{array}$$

Cross out the 3 tens and write a 2 above it to show that you now have 2 tens. Write a 1 next to the ones to show that you now have 12 ones (or cross it out and write 12 above it.)

$$\begin{array}{r} 2\ \ \ \\ 4\ 1\ \not{3}\ {}^{1}2 \\ -\ 1\ 6\ 7\ 9 \\ \hline \end{array}$$

Subtract the ones. Write the difference under the line in the ones place.

$$\begin{array}{r} 2\ \ \ \\ 4\ 1\ \not{3}\ {}^{1}2 \\ -\ 1\ 6\ 7\ 9 \\ \hline 3 \end{array}$$

There are not enough tens to take away 7 tens, so rename a hundred for 10 tens.

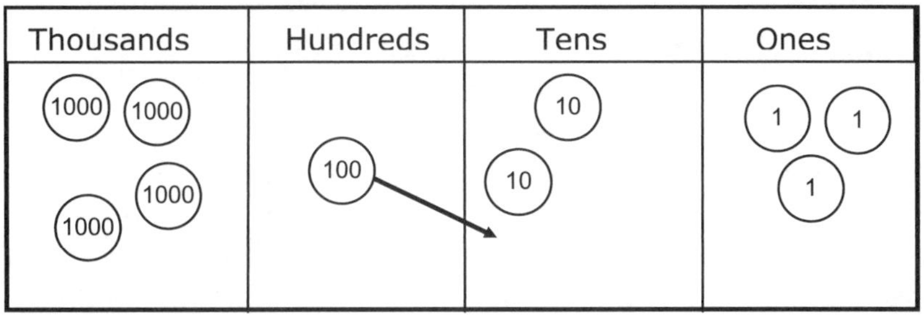

Cross out the 1 in the hundreds place and write a 0 above it. Write a 1 next to the 2 above the tens to show there are 12 tens.

$$\begin{array}{r} 0\ {}^{1}2\ \ \ \\ 4\ \ \not{1}\ \ \not{3}\ {}^{1}2 \\ -\ 1\ \ 6\ \ 7\ \ 9 \\ \hline 3 \end{array}$$

Remove 7 tens.

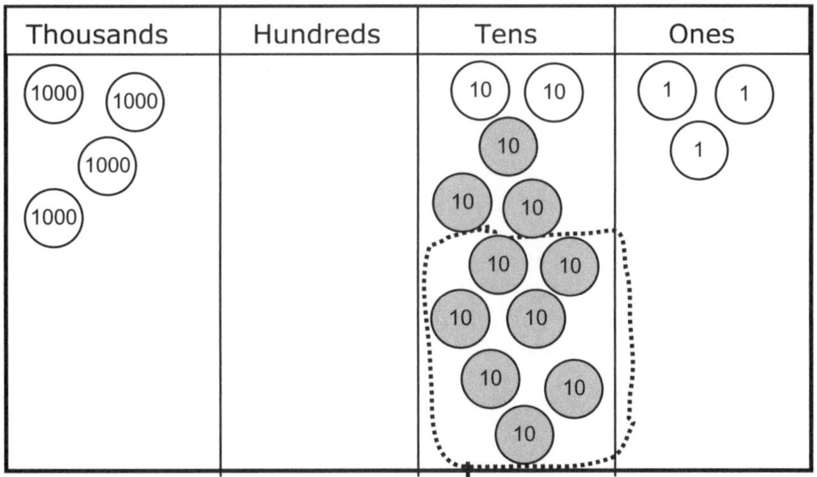

Subtract the tens. Write the difference under the line in the tens place.

$$\begin{array}{r} 0\ {}^{1}2\ \ \ \\ 4\ \ \not{1}\ \ \not{3}\ {}^{1}2 \\ -\ 1\ \ 6\ \ 7\ \ 9 \\ \hline 5\ \ 3 \end{array}$$

Rename a thousand for ten hundreds and remove 5 hundreds and then 1 thousand.

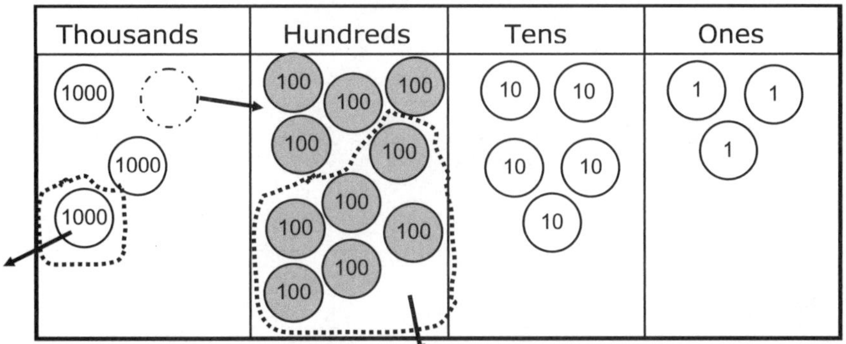

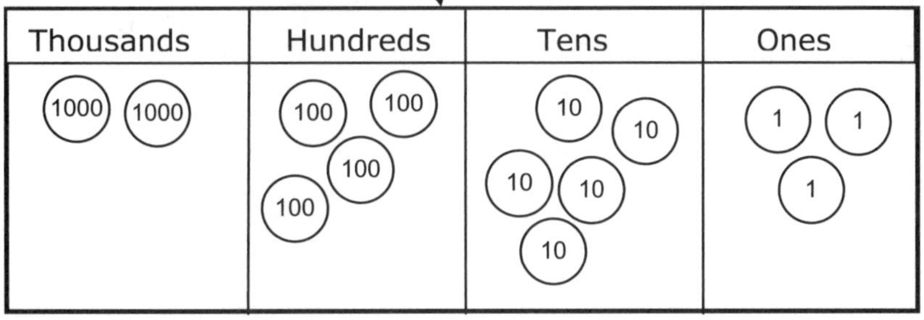

Cross out the 4 thousands, write a 3 above it. Write a 1 next to the 0 to show 10 hundreds. Subtract the hundreds, write the difference under the line in the hundreds place. Subtract the thousands, and write the result under the line in the thousands place.

$$\begin{array}{r} 3\ {}^{1}0\ {}^{1}2\ \ \ \\ \not{4}\ \ \not{1}\ \ \not{3}\ {}^{1}2 \\ -\ 1\ \ 6\ \ 7\ \ 9 \\ \hline 2\ \ 4\ \ 5\ \ 3 \end{array}$$

(1) Renaming Ones, Tens, or Hundreds (pp. 28-30)

Subtract 4-digit numbers where the ones, tens, or hundreds are renamed.

Trade-In

Material: **Number discs**, **place value chart**, and **playing cards** with the face cards removed and tens made into 0 or four sets of number cards 0 – 9.

Single player: Place some thousands discs on the place value chart. Draw a card. The number drawn represents the number of hundreds that need to be removed. A thousand will have to be traded for 10 hundreds to remove hundreds. Draw another card. This number is the number of tens that must be removed. Trade in a hundred for 10 tens to remove tens. Draw a third card. This is the number of ones that must be removed. Trade a ten for 10 ones and remove ones. Continue to draw three cards, removing first hundreds, then tens, then ones. Repeat until there are no more thousands.

Learning Tasks 1-5, pp. 29-30

In learning task 1, there is no renaming. They may be rewritten vertically, but your student may be able to keep track of the place values of each digit without rewriting. In learning task 5, there is one renaming. Rewrite the problems vertically. Illustrate with number discs if necessary.

1. (a) 6844 (b) 6827
   (c) 6347 (d) 2847
   (e) 6324 (f) 2324
2. 5334
3. 4420
4. 6700
5. (a) 4307 (b) 4328
   (c) 6282 (d) 5477
   (e) 8821 (f) 2625

Trade-In (variation)

See directions above.

Single-player: Write the subtraction problems down on paper as the game is played rather than using manipulatives. Start with a number such as 3,000.

Multi-player: Players take turns drawing cards. The first one to rename the last thousand wins.

Workbook Exercise 10

(2) Renaming More Than Once (pp. 30-31)

Subtract 4-digit numbers where renaming occurs three times.

Learning Tasks 6-9, pp. 30-31

Illustrate these with number discs, if necessary.

7. (a) 7428 (b) 4188
   (c) 3791 (d) 2714
   (e) 5666 (f) 1833

9. (a) 1897 (b) 2879
   (c) 4781 (d) 1097

The Smallest Difference

Material: Use **playing cards** with the face cards and tens removed or 4 sets of number cards 1-9.

Procedure: Shuffle cards and draw 4 cards. Aces are ones. The student must arrange the numbers into two 2-digit numbers such that the difference is the smallest number possible. Practice with 2-digit numbers, then try 3-digit numbers (using 6 cards). After the student can find the smallest difference with 3-digit numbers try 4-digit numbers (using 8 cards).

Game 1. Deal 8 cards to each player, one at a time. As each player receives a card, he or she must decide where to place it in a 4 x 2 arrangement to make two 4-digit numbers. Once placed, the card cannot be rearranged. After each player has received all 8 cards, they subtract their numbers. The player with the smallest answer wins.

Game 2 (harder). The 8 cards are arranged into any two 4-digit numbers after all have been dealt.

Workbook Exercise 11

(3) Renaming Over Several Place-Values (pp. 32-33)

Subtract 4-digit numbers where renaming occurs over more than one place value.

Work through a problem such as 5000 – 684 using number discs and writing each step at a time, and then have your student do the same with another problem, such as 6000 – 457.

There are no ones, but there are no tens or hundreds to rename. One of the thousands has to be renamed. Cross it out, write 4 above it, and show that there are now 10 hundreds.

$$\begin{array}{rrrr} 4 & & & \\ \not{5} & {}^{1}0 & 0 & 0 \\ - & 6 & 8 & 4 \\ \hline \end{array}$$

Now, one of the hundreds needs to be renamed, leaving 9 hundreds. Show that there are now 10 tens and 9 hundreds.

$$\begin{array}{rrrr} 4 & 9 & & \\ \not{5} & {}^{1}\not{0} & {}^{1}0 & 0 \\ - & 6 & 8 & 4 \\ \hline \end{array}$$

Finally, one of the tens has to be renamed. Show that there are now 10 ones and 9 tens.

Then subtract.

$$\begin{array}{rrrr} 4 & 9 & 9 & \\ \not{5} & {}^{1}\not{0} & {}^{1}\not{0} & {}^{1}0 \\ - & 6 & 8 & 4 \\ \hline 4 & 3 & 1 & 6 \end{array}$$

Learning Tasks 10-14, pp. 32-33

12. (a) 3608 (b) 2155
 (c) 590 (d) 2926

14. (a) 4578 (b) 6155
 (c) 5128 (d) 684
 (e) 1587 (f) 4279

Play **The Smallest Difference**, but include 0's. If using playing cards, you can use an old set and white out the 1 in 10.

Workbook Exercise 12

Part 4 Two-step Word Problems

(1) Two-Step Word Problems (pp. 36-37)

Solve two-step word problems.

In Primary Mathematics 2 and in earlier sections of Primary Mathematics 3A, students have solved problems involving two steps where they were given both an (a) and (b) part to solve – the answer to the (a) part was used in the (b) part. Here, the student will be solving two-step word problems where they must determine the intermediate step themselves. Modeling can be used to help solve the problem.

Page 36 and Learning Tasks 1-2, pp. 36-37

As you go through these, ask your students pertinent questions so that they look at each bit of information given in the problem, such as:

> What do we need to find?
> What do we need to know to find this?
> What information are we given?
> How can we find what we first need to know?
> Now that we have that answer, how do we find the answer to the problem?

You may want to have them draw a model for the problem on p. 36 and for learning task 1. Ask them to identify which part of the model represents which piece of information from the problem.

29 – 20 = **9**

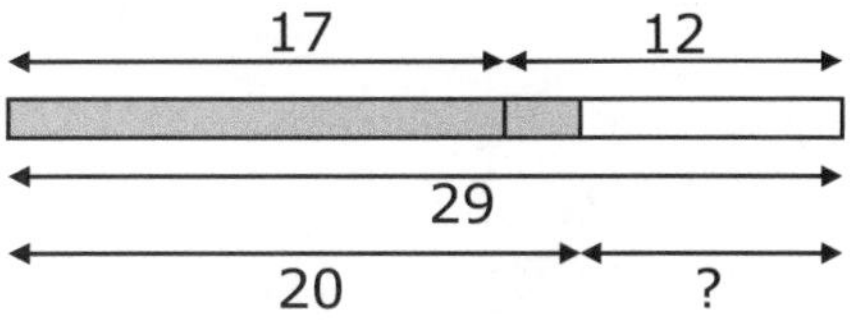

1. 71 – 54 = **17**

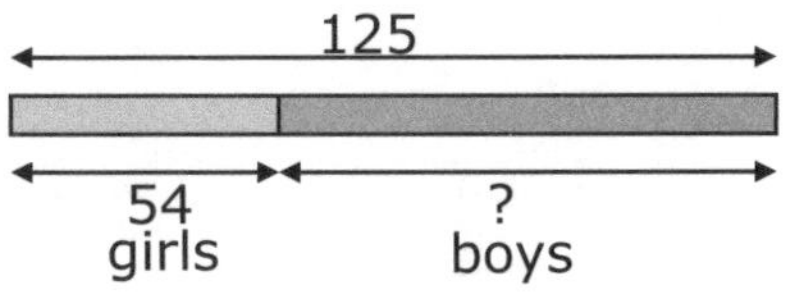

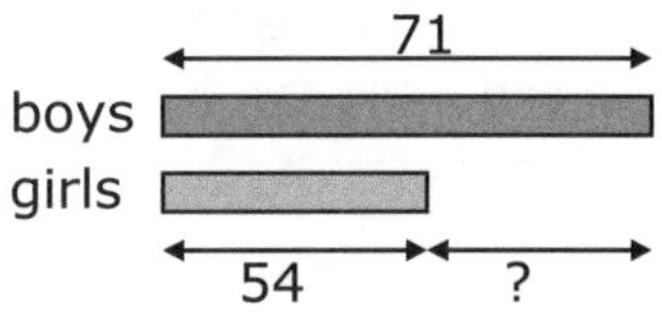

2. 137 + 164 = **301**

Workbook Exercise 13
Workbook Review 1

Enrichment 2 – Mental Math

In Primary Mathematics 1 and 2, the student learned to mentally subtract numbers with one regrouping in ones, such as

45 – 8

We can do this either as

45 – 8 = 30 + 15 – 8 = 30 + 7 = 37

Or as

45 – 8 = 30 + (10 – 8) + 5 = 30 + 2 + 5 = 30 + 7 = 37
("subtracting from a ten" with the 8)

In either case, before writing down the tens, we can "look ahead" to see if there will be one less ten. In

345 – 8

we can first write down the hundreds (3), and then subtract 45 – 8 as above, writing down the tens first and then the ones.

We can now mentally subtract a 1-digit number from a 4-digit number, such as

2345 – 8

by writing down first the thousands, then the hundreds, then "looking ahead" before writing down the tens:

2345 – 8 = 2337

This "mental regrouping" has also been done with tens, such as

450 – 80 = 370

Here, we can think 45 tens – 8 tens, and subtract the same way as subtracting ones above, and then writing a 0 for tens. The student also learned to mentally subtract

452 – 80 = 372

by subtracting tens as above (450 – 80) then writing down the ones. This can be extended to hundreds:

4500 – 800 = 3700

Here, regrouping occurs only in the hundreds, and we can "look ahead" before writing down the thousands to see if subtracting the hundreds will decrease the thousands by 1. This procedure can also be followed in

4502 – 808 = 3702

We can subtract 4500 and 800, and write down 37, then 0 for no tens, then 2 for ones. In

4562 – 842 = 3720

We can first subtract 4500 and 800 to get 3700, write down 37, then subtract the tens and then the ones:

4562 – 842 = 4500 – 800 + 62 – 42 = 3720

These types of problems are given in Mental Math 8.
Go through these procedures with thousands, and then help your student work through the ones on the Mental Math page.

Enrichment 3 – Mental Math

In Primary Mathematics 2, the student learned to add and subtract 99 or 98 to or from 3 digit numbers. This was extended down to numbers ending in 95 in the context of adding and subtracting money. To add a number close to 100, we can add 100 and then subtract the difference between that number and 100:

$$456 + 95 = 456 + 100 - 5 = 556 - 5 = 551$$

This idea can be used with 3 digit numbers that end in 95-99.

$$456 + 295 = 456 + 300 - 5 = 756 - 5 = 751$$

This can be done with 4-digit numbers as well:

$$3456 + 295 = 3456 + 300 - 5 = 3756 - 5 = 3751$$

To subtract a number close to 100, we can subtract 100 and then add the difference between that number and 100:

$$456 - 97 = 456 - 100 + 3 = 356 + 3 = 359$$

This idea can be used with 3 digit numbers that end in 90-99:

$$456 - 297 = 456 - 300 + 3 = 156 + 3 = 159$$

It can be done with 4-digit numbers as well:

$$3456 - 297 = 3456 - 300 + 3 = 3156 + 3 = 159$$

In Primary Mathematics 2, students also learned to make 100:

35 + ____ = 100 or 100 – 35 = ____

The number in the blank can be found by either counting up first by tens and then ones, or by thinking of the number which when added to the ten makes 9 for the tens place and the number which added to the ones to makes 10 for the ones place. The tens digit would be 6 (3 + **6** = 9) and the ones digit 5 (5 + **5** = 10) to give 65.

If there is no value in the ones place, then find the answer as if the problem had one less digit. Think of the number which when added to the ten makes 10.

100 – 60 = 40 (Solve as 10 – 6, but add a 0 to the answer.)

The tens digit in the answer is 4 (6 + **4** = 10).

For 400 – 35 = ______

subtract 100, and make 100 with 35:

$$400 - 35 = 400 - 100 + 100 - 35 = 300 + 65 = 365$$

In 1000 – 456 =______

make 1000. Look at the hundreds digit of the second number. Find the difference between that number and 9. That is the hundreds digit. Look at the tens digit. Find the difference between that number and 9. That is the tens digit. Look at the ones digit. Find the difference between that number and 10. That is the ones digit.

1000 – 456 = (900 – 400) + (90 – 50) + (10 – 6) = 500 + 40 + 4 = 544

For 1000 – 35

Think of 35 as 035. The hundreds digit of the answer would be 9 (0 + **9** = 9), then tens digit 6 (3 + **6** = 9) and the ones digit 5 (5 + **5** = 10) to give 965.

If there are no ones digit in the second number, solve the problem as if there were no ones digit. The tens must make 10.

1000 – 340 = 660

For the hundred, 3 + 6 = **9**, and for the tens, 4 + 6 = **10**. There are no ones.

These types of problems are given in Mental Math 9. Go through some of these procedures with your student, illustrating with number discs if necessary.

Unit 3 Multiplication and Division

Part 1 Looking Back

(1) Review of Multiplication (pp. 39-40)

Review multiplication concepts.

In Primary Mathematics 2, the student learned multiplication as repeated addition, and that multiplication is commutative. They also learned the multiplication facts of 2, 3, 4, 5, and 10. This section reviews the concept of multiplication and covers multiplication by 0. Spend some time practicing the multiplication facts of 1, 3, 4, 5, and 10. By Part 3 of this unit, the student should know these facts. Some suggested activities are given here.

The order in which the factors are written is not significant. Do not require the student to learn the term **commutative** yet.

Use **linking cubes** or other small objects. Have your student arrange the 24 cubes in a rectangular array and write the corresponding multiplication sentences. For example, he arranges them in a six by four array. He writes 4 x 6 = 24 and 6 x 4 = 24. If necessary, remind him that the array can be interpreted as 4 groups of 6 or 6 groups of 4.

4 x 6 can mean 4 times 6: 6 + 6 + 6 + 6 or
4 x 6 can mean 4, 6 times (6 times 4): 4 + 4 + 4 + 4 + 4 + 4

Page 39
Have your student supply the missing numbers.

Learning Task 1, p. 40

1. 12; 12; 12; 12

Fact Practice

Material: A set of **fact cards** for the multiplication and division facts 2, 3, 4, 5 and 10. Include some cards for 1 times a number or a number divided by 1 and, after lesson B below, for 0 times a number.

Procedure: Shuffle and show your student each card. If he gets the correct answer, put it in one pile; if not, put it in another pile. Repeat with the second pile until all the cards are in the "correct" pile.

War

Material: **Playing cards** with the face cards removed, **or** four sets **of number cards** 1-10. **Dice** with the 6 covered up with tape and a 10 written on it.

Procedure: Shuffle the cards and deal all out. Leave the cards face down in a pile in front of each player. Each player throws a die and turns over a card. Each player multiplies the card number by the number on the die. The player with the largest product gets all the cards. If two players have the same product, the one with the highest card gets the cards. The winner is the one with the most cards after all the cards are turned over.

Variation: Use two decks of cards. Use only the black cards ace through 10 from one deck. Use all the red cards ace through 5 and the 10s from the same deck. Use the red cards 2-5 from the second deck. Make two decks from these cards, one of black cards only and one of red cards only. Deal out the cards separately so that each player has a pile of black cards and a pile of red cards. Each player turns over one card from each pile and multiplies the numbers together. The player with the largest product gets all the cards. The winner is the one with the most cards after all the cards are turned over.

Workbook Exercise 14 and 15

(2) Review of Division (p. 40)

Review division concepts.

In Primary Mathematics 1 and 2, two division situations were taught; sharing and grouping.

In sharing, we are given the total and the number of equal groups, and we divide to find out how many are in each group.

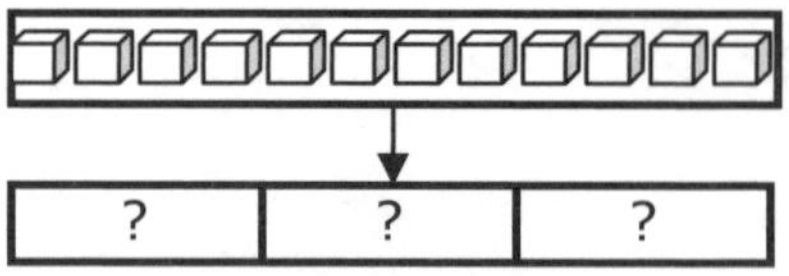

In grouping, we are given the total and the number that needs to go in each group, and we divide to find out how many groups there are.

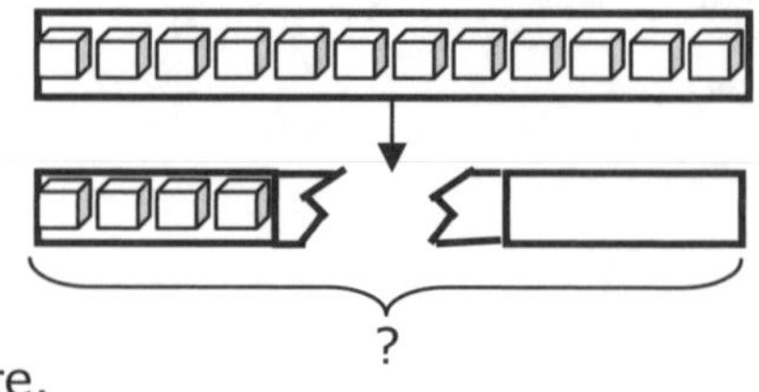

The students were also taught to relate division facts to multiplication facts. This is reviewed here.

➤ Remind your student, if necessary, that the division facts are related to multiplication facts.

To find the answer to 15 ÷ 5, we can think of the number times 5 that gives 15

15 ÷ 5 = _____ _____ x 5 = 15 $15 \underset{\times 5}{\overset{\div 5}{\rightleftarrows}} 3$

Learning Task 2, p. 40

2. 7 10 7 4

➤ Spend some time practicing the division facts of 1, 3, 4, 5, and 10. By Part 3 of this unit, the student should know these facts. A suggested game is given here.

Divide It

Material: A set of **number cards** with the multiples of 2, 3, 4, 5, and 10 up to 10 times the number (50 cards). **Dice** with the 6 replaced with a ten, one for each player, or the cards 2-6 and 10 from a deck of **playing cards** for each player, shuffled and placed face down for each player.

Procedure: Shuffle the number cards and turn over 5 cards. Place the cards in the center. Each player throws a die or turns over a card. If the player can evenly divide a number on one of the cards in the middle by the number on his die or card, and give the correct answer, he gets the card. Each player tries to get as many cards as possible each round. For the next round, deal out more cards to replace the cards taken from the middle. The player with the most cards after all have been turned over wins.

Variation: Players take turns throwing the die. If there are any numbers in the center that are multiples of the number on the die, the player gets those cards. New cards are turned over to replace the cards removed before the next player throws the die. The player with the most cards after all have been turned over and each player has had to pass once.

Workbook Exercise 16

(3) Zero in Multiplication and Division (p. 41)

Multiply a number by 0.

Use **cubes** or other small objects. Draw 4 circles or set out 4 bowls. Have your student place 3 cubes in each circle or bowl and write the multiplication fact.

$3 \times 4 = 12$ or $4 \times 3 = 12$

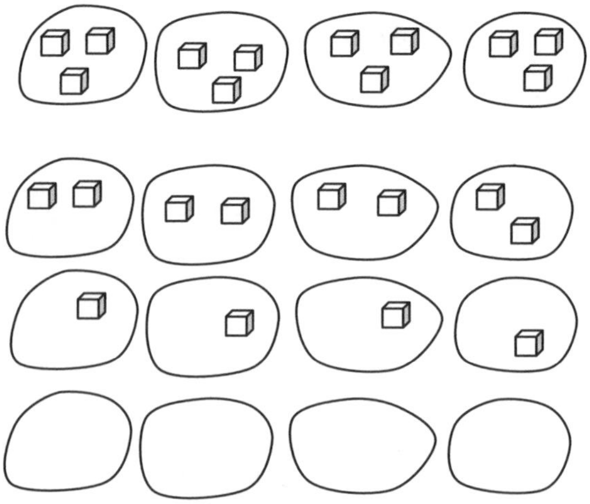

Remove one cube from each circle and have her write the multiplication facts.

$2 \times 4 = 8$ or $4 \times 2 = 8$

Repeat with another cube.

$1 \times 4 = 4$ or $4 \times 1 = 4$

Repeat with the last cube.

$0 \times 4 = 0$ or $4 \times 0 = 0$

Point out that if you have 0 objects in each group, there are 0 objects total. Ask her for the total if you had no groups of 4 objects. (0)

Zero multiplied by any number is zero.
Any number multiplied by zero is zero.

Tell her you have 0 objects. You want to divide them up among 4 people. How many would each person get? (0)

$0 \div 4 = 0$

Zero divided by any number is zero.

Tell her it is mathematically impossible to divide a number by 0. Write

$8 \div 2 = 4 \rightarrow 4 \times 2 = 8$
$8 \div 0 = \_\_ \rightarrow \_\_ \times 0 = 8$

There is no number times 0 that would give 8, since any number times zero equals zero. So you cannot divide a number by 0.

Ask your student:

What is any number times 1? (The number.)
What is a number divided by itself? (1)
What is a number divided by 1? (The number.)

Learning Tasks 3-4, p. 41

3.	(a) 6	(b) 4	(c) 2	(d) 0
4.	(a) 6	(b) 4	(c) 2	(d) 0

Concentration

Material: Index cards

Procedure: Write the facts your student is having the most difficulty with on index cards. Write the answers on other cards. Be careful that the writing can't be seen on the other side of the cards. Arrange the cards in an array face down. The student turns over two cards at a time. If they match (for example, 4 x 8 matches with 32) he removes the card, if they don't match he turns them over again in the same place.

➤ You may wish to have your student begin to practice counting by sixes, sevens, eights, and nines. You can draw a ladder, and say that each rung is 6 cm or in. higher, and that he needs to give the height up to each rung, one after the other. Then each day he can practice his 6 ladder, or 7 ladder, etc. He can also go down, counting by sixes backwards from 60. In the U.S. multiples of 12 are common, for example in converting feet to inches, so you may want to include the 11th and 12th rungs.

Workbook Exercise 17

(4) Word Problems (p. 42)

Solve simple word problems involving multiplication and division.

Use this section to introduce your student to the part-whole model for multiplication and division problems, if you did not already do so in Primary Mathematics 2. There are two kinds of models that can be used for word problems involving multiplication and division, a part-whole model and a comparison model. In this section we will use the part-whole model. The comparison model will be taught in the next section. These models are based on the concept of a unit. The term "unit" will be introduced in the next session. Do not require your student to draw models for every exercise if he can solve the problem without a model.

Learning Task 5, p. 42

Read and discuss the problem with your student as follows.

We need to find the total number of buttons.
We are given the number of cards (parts) and the number of buttons on each card.
We can represent each card with a bar. 
The bar is the part.
How many bars would we draw to show all 5 cards? (5 bars)
We want to find the total, so we put them end to end.

We can label one part as 8 to show how many buttons are on each card. We don't have to label all the parts since we know they are all the same.
Then we can show that we need to find the total by labeling the total bar.

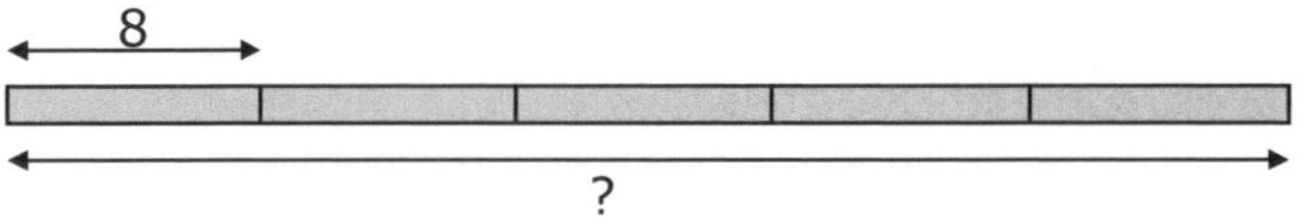

We could draw a bar representing the total first, and then divide it up into 5 equal parts. We need to find a total:

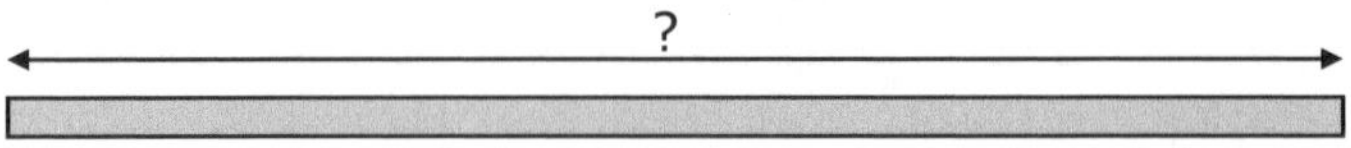

We know the number of cards (parts) and the number in each part, so we divide the bar up into 5 parts. We know the 5 parts are equal, even if in the hand drawing we can't get them exactly equal:

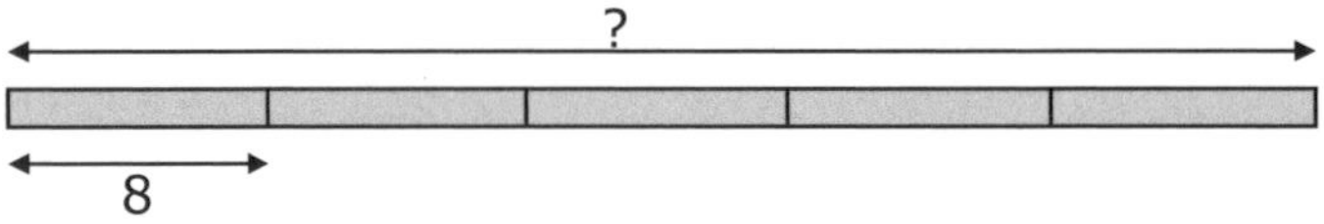

To find the total number of buttons, we multiply the number in each part by the number of parts.

8 x 5 = **40**

➤ Write and discuss the following problem:

4 boys shared 36 toy cars equally. How many toys cars did each boy get?

We draw a bar to show the total, and label it.

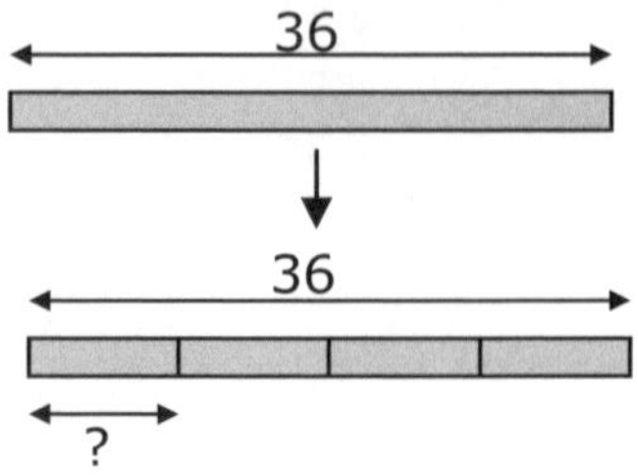

There are 4 boys (parts or groups). Each boy is getting the same number of cars, so we divide the bar up into 4 equal parts, one part for each boy. We want to find out how many cars will go into each part.
How do we find the number of cars for each part?
(We divide)
36 ÷ 4 = 9
Each boy gets **9** cars.

Learning Task 6, p. 42

Discuss the problem with your student.

What do we need to find? (The number of dresses.)
The cloth is cut into pieces, one for each dress. If we find the number of pieces of cloth, does this give us the number of dresses she makes? (Yes)
We can draw a bar to show the total length of all the dresses. We don't really know how many parts to divide it up into, but we know that each part has 3 meters in it. We can show that we need to find the number of parts with an opening in the bar, since the length of the bar (number of parts) depends on how many parts there are.

How do we find the number of parts?
(We divide.)
$21 \div 3 = 7$
He made **7** dresses.

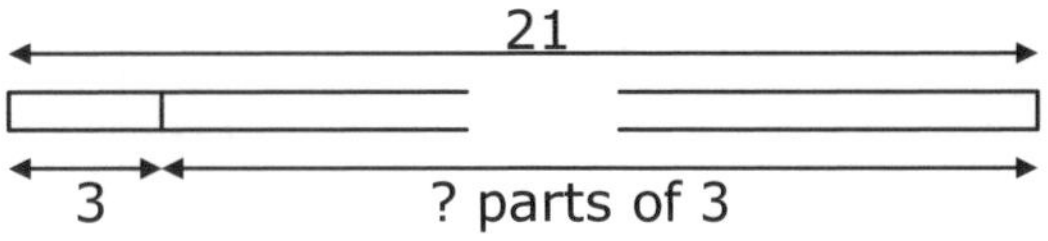

Optional:
Explain to your student that since 3 x ____ = 21 is the same as _____ x 3 = 21, he can also diagram it by dividing the bar up into 3 equal parts. Each part represents 1 of the meters. He can think of it as first assigning 1 m to each dress, which is the first part. The value for each part would be how many times he assigned a meter for a dress, and so would be the number of dresses. He then assigns a second meter for each dress to give the second part, and finally he assigns a third meter to each dress, to give the third part. The value of each part would then be the number of dresses he has. This may be difficult for your student to conceptualize. You can give a problem such as

> There are some children at a party. I have 21 candies and I give each child 3 candies, one round at a time. There are no candies left. How many children are there?

In this case, you draw a bar for the total number of candies, and divide it up into 3 parts. The first part represents the first round of handing out candies, so its value is the number of children. The second part represents the second round, and the third part represents the third round. 27 is divided into 3 parts (rounds). Each round is 7 ($21 \div 3 = 7$). There are 7 children.

Workbook Exercise 18

Part 2 More Word Problems

(1) One-Step Word Problems (pp. 44-46)

Associate multiplication with how many times **as many** or how many times **as much** or **how many times more**.
Use pictorial models to solve word problems involving multiplication and division.
Understand and use the concept of a **unit**.

In the comparison model for multiplication and division, two quantities are compared. One is a multiple of the other. Each equal part can be called a **unit**.

If the smaller quantity, or value for one part, is given, we can find the larger quantity by multiplication.

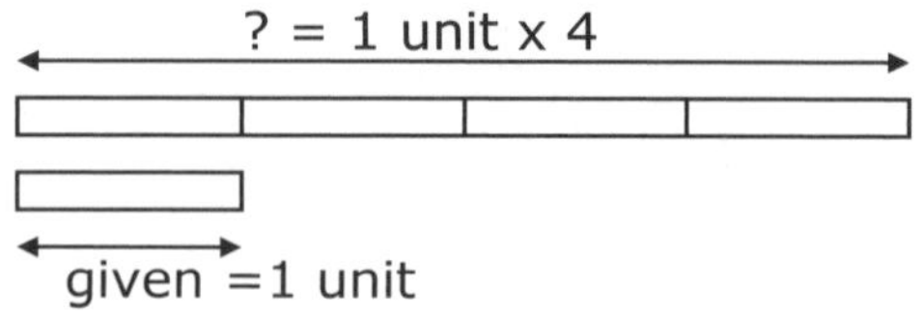

If the larger quantity is given, we can find the smaller quantity, or the unit, by division. Once this unit is found, we use multiplication to find other multiples, such the difference between the two quantities or the total for both quantities.

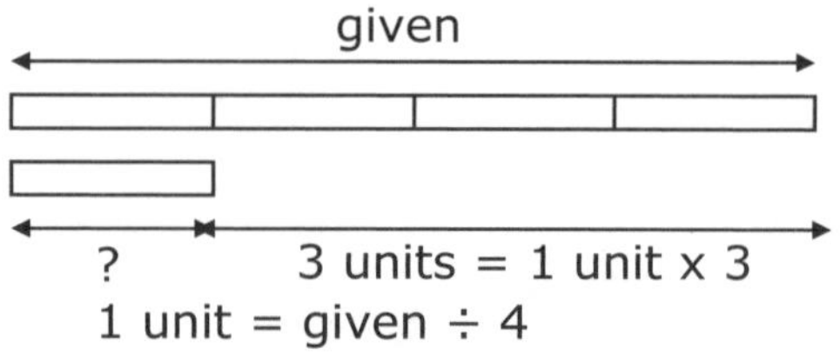

Use two different kinds of objects, such as pencils and crayons. Tell your student to count out 3 pencils and three times as many crayons as pencils. She should have 9 of the second object.
Show her that she can draw a pictorial model to show that she has three times as many crayons as pencils. Each bar is a **unit** and represents 3 objects. The unit is the number of pencils.
1 unit = 3.

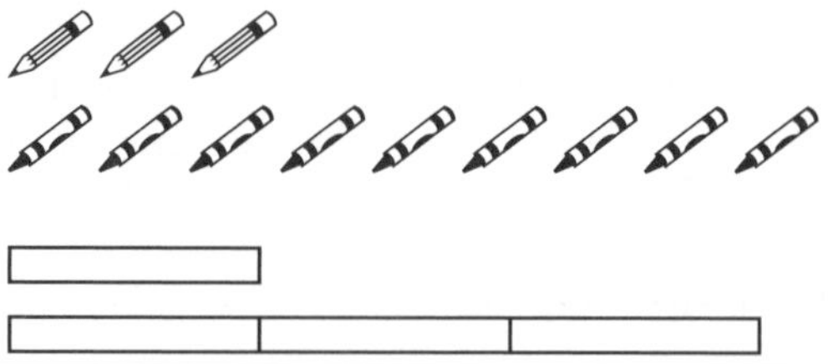

Ask:
How many units of pencils are there? (1)
How many units of crayons are there? (3)

The number of crayons is 3 times the number of pencils.
3 units = 1 unit x 3 = 3 x 3 = 9

How many units more crayons than pencils are there? (2)
How many total units are there? (4)

Discuss problems such as the following with your student, using pictorial models.

There are 5 times as many red blocks as blue blocks. There are 4 blue blocks.

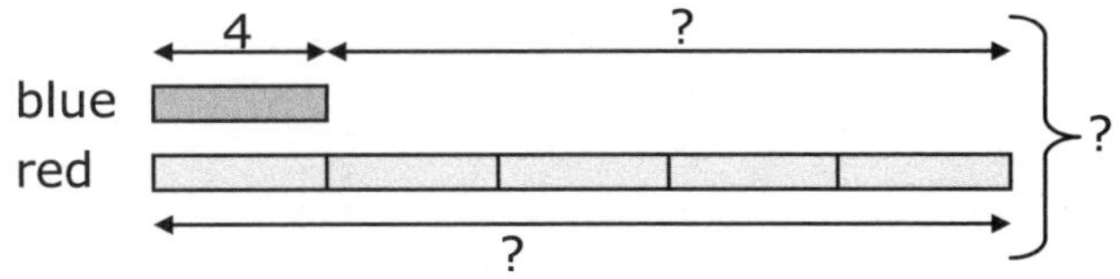

What is 1 unit?	Number of blue blocks = 1 unit
How much is 1 unit?	1 unit = 4
How many units of red blocks are there?	Number of red blocks = 5 units
How many red blocks are there?	5 units = 4 x 5 = 20
How many more units of red blocks than blue blocks are there?	Red blocks – blue blocks = 4 units
How many more red blocks than blue blocks are there?	4 units = 4 x 4 = 16 or Difference = 20 - 4 = 16
How many total units are there?	Total blocks = 6 units
How many block are there altogether?	6 units = 4 x 6 = 24 or total = 20 + 4 = 24

There are 3 times as many blue blocks as red blocks. There are 21 blue blocks.

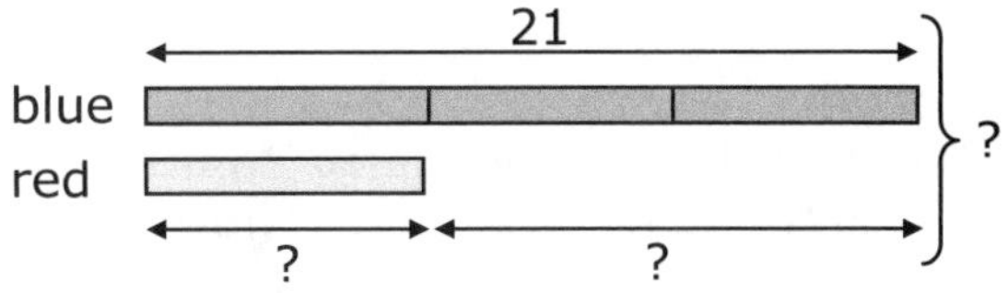

What is 1 unit?	Number of red blocks = 1 unit
How many units of blue blocks are there?	Number of blue blocks = 3 units.
How many blocks are there in 3 units?	3 units = 21
How many red blocks are there?	1 unit = 21 ÷ 3 = 7
How many more units of blue blocks than red blocks are there?	Blue blocks - red blocks = 2 units
How many more blue blocks than red blocks are there?	2 units = 7 x 2 = 14 or Difference = 21 - 7 = 14
How many total units are there?	Total blocks = 4 units
How many total blocks are there?	4 units = 7 x 4 = 28 or Total = 21 + 7 = 28

There are five times more red blocks than blue blocks. There are 50 more red blocks than blue blocks.

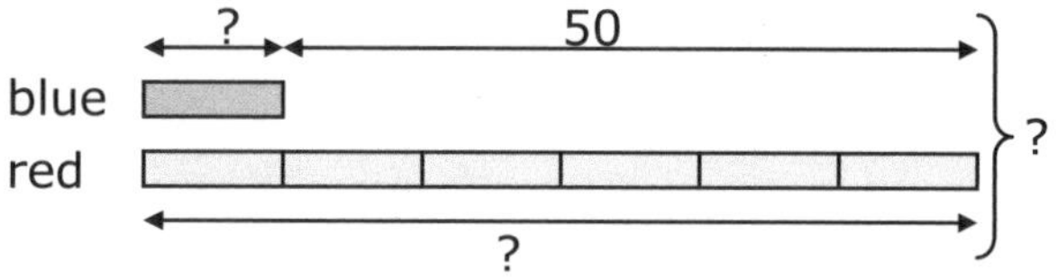

What is 1 unit?	Number of blue blocks = 1 unit
How many units more red blocks than blue blocks are there.	More red than blue = 5 units
How many units red blocks are there?	Number of red blocks = 6 units
How many blocks are there in 5 units?	5 units = 50
How many blocks are there in 1 unit?	1 unit = 50 ÷ 5 = 10
How many blue blocks are there?	1 unit = 10
How many red blocks are there?	6 units = 10 x 6 = 60 or Number of red blocks = 10 + 50 = 60
How many total units are there?	Total blocks = 7 units
How many total blocks are there?	7 units = 10 x 7 = 70 or Total = 10 + 60 = 70 or Total = 10 + 10 + 50 = 70

Page 44 and Learning Tasks 1-3, pp. 45-46
Go through these pages with your student.

Learning Task 1: We are comparing two quantities, so we can draw a comparison model. She has $**8**.

Learning Task 2: We have a whole, and we need to find out the amount in each part, so we can draw a part-whole model. Point out that one part is called a unit. Each child paid $**7**

Learning Task 3: We have equal parts and need to find a total, so we can draw a part-whole model. The cost of the present was $**30**.

Do other examples if necessary.

Your student should continue reviewing the multiplication and division facts, and can continue to practice counting by sixes, sevens, eights, and nines.

Workbook Exercise 19

(2) Two-Step Word Problems (p. 46)

Solve two-step word problems using all four operations.

The student can follow a procedure similar to that outlined in the previous section to solve problems involving both multiplication and division as well as addition and subtraction, but in this section he will have to determine the intermediate step himself. Using a pictorial model will help him to determine the intermediate step. There can be more than one approach to solving these problems. Allow your student to develop his own approach.

Some problems can be solved by using a part-whole model where one part is a multiple of a unit.

If one part is given, and the other part is a multiple of a given unit, we can find the total by first finding one part by multiplication, then adding the second part.

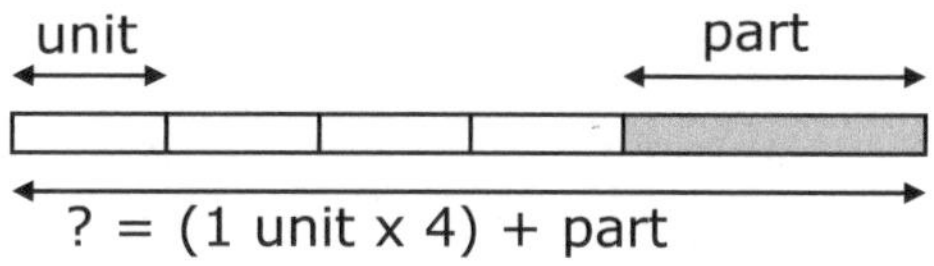

If the total and one part is given, and the second part is a multiple of a unit, we can find the unit by first subtracting to find the part, and then dividing to find the unit.

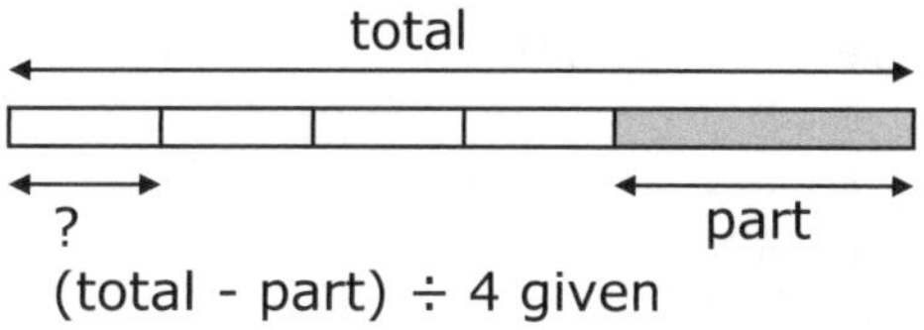

Modeling is a tool that can be used in solving word problems. Some students can work out solutions to the problems in the workbook and practices mentally or without a drawn pictorial model. Your student should be able to draw a pictorial representation when necessary, but do not insist that he always draw one if it is not necessary for him to do so to solve the problem.

Learning Task 4, p. 46
Discuss this problem with your student.
The farmer has **28** more chickens than ducks.

You may wish to discuss an alternative solution:
There are 4 more units of chickens than ducks.
1 unit = 7.
4 units = 4 x 1 unit = 4 x 7 = 28.
You can also ask your student for the number of ducks and chickens the farmer has altogether.
Total ducks and chickens = total chickens + total ducks = 7 + 35 = 42.

➤ Discuss other problems, such as the following ones, using pictorial models. Help your student model the problem. A suggested solution is given, but your student may come up with a different approach. Help him determine an approach, rather than giving him one.

Sam bought 4 toy cars and a toy airplane. Each toy car cost $5. The airplane cost $12. How much money did he spend? How much more did he spend on the cars than on the airplane?

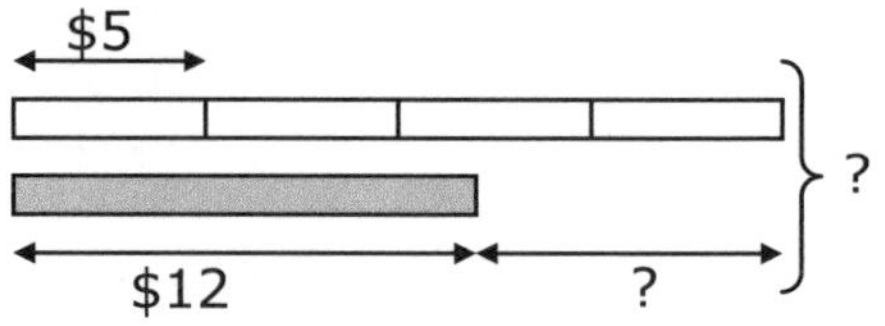

There are two parts, the cost of the toy cars and the cost of the toy airplane. The cost of the toy cars has 4 units. We need to find the total cost of the cars first.
1 unit = the cost of one toy car.
Total cost of cars = 4 units = 4 x $5 = $20
Total money spent = $20 + $12 = $32
Amount more money spent on cars = $20 - $12 = $8

Mary bought 3 dresses. Each dress cost the same amount. She gave the cashier $20 and got $2 change. How much did each dress cost?

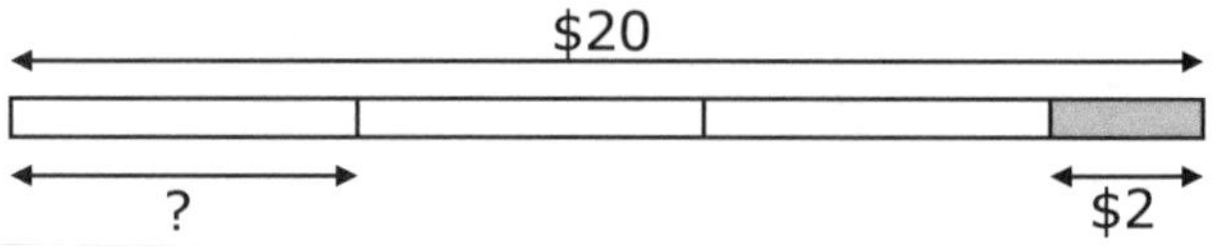

The total is $20. One part is the change, and the other the cost of the dresses. We want to find the cost of 1 dress. We need to find the cost of all the dresses first.
Cost of the dresses = $20 - $2 = $18
Cost of 1 dress = $18 ÷ 3 = $6

Peter has $12. He has twice as much money as Paul. John has $2 less than Paul. How much money does John have?

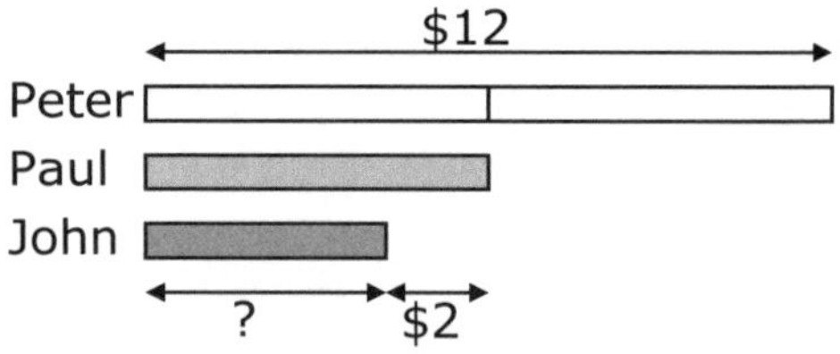

If John has $2 less than Paul, we need to find out how much money Paul has. We can find that by division.
Paul's money = 1 unit
Peter's money = 2 units
2 units = $12
1 unit = $12 ÷ 2 = $6
John's money = Paul's money - $2 = $6 - $2 = $4

Workbook Exercise 20

Workbook Exercise 28
This is a review of the multiplication and division facts of 2, 3, 4, 5, and 10. Your student should have a good knowledge of these facts by now, and should know them for the next part, so it would be appropriate to do this exercise now.

Part 3 Multiplying Ones, Tens and Hundreds

(1) Multiplication of Tens and Hundreds with Ones (pp. 49-50)

Multiply tens and hundreds by a 1-digit number.
Relate the term **product** to multiplication.

In this part, the student will be learning how to multiply a 2-digit or 3-digit number by a 1-digit number using the multiplication algorithm. It is important that the student has a good knowledge of place value.

Give your students some problems such as the following:

2 ones = 2
20 ones = 20 = ____ tens
20 tens = 200 = ____ hundreds
20 hundreds = 2000 = ____ thousands
24 ones = 24 = _____ tens _____ ones
24 tens = 240 = ______ hundreds ______ tens
24 hundreds = 2400 = _______ thousands ______ hundreds

Illustrate with **number discs** if necessary. For example, give him 24 tens, and have him trade in 20 tens for 2 hundreds.

Use **base-10 blocks** or **number discs**. Set out an array of 2 rows of 4 ones, then two rows of 4 tens, then two rows of 4 hundreds. Ask your student how many there are. There are 8. Write

2 x 4 = 8 or 4 x 2 = 8

How many elephants would there be if there were 2 rows of 4 elephants in each row?

2 x 4 elephants = 8 elephants

How many cars would there be if there were 2 rows of 4 cars in each row?

2 x 4 cars = 8 cars

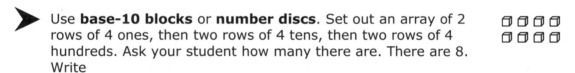

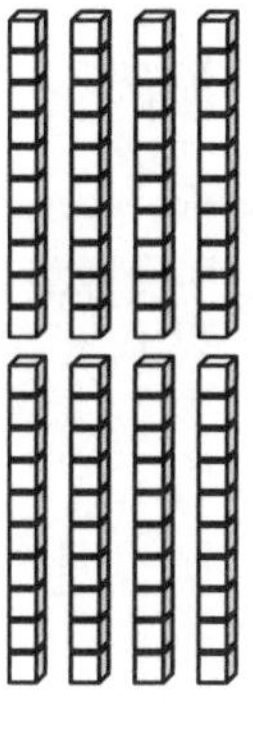

How many tens would there be if there were 2 rows of 4 tens in each row?

2 x 4 tens = 8 tens
2 x 40 = 80

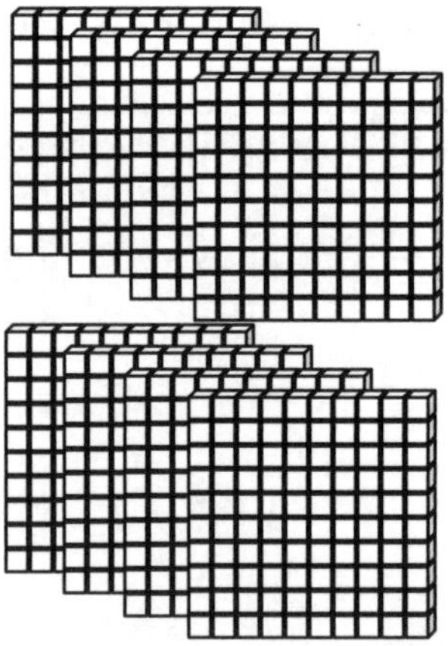

How many hundreds would there be if there were 2 piles of 4 hundreds in each pile?

2 x 4 hundreds = 8 hundreds
2 x 400 = 800

Cover up the two 0's in the 400 and the two 0's in 800:

Two times 4 equals eight.

Uncover the 0's:

Two times 4 hundred equals 8 hundred.

Discussion

Write:

When we multiply two numbers together, the answer is called the **product**. What is the **product** of 5 and 3?

5 x **3** = **15**

What is the product of 50 and 3?
5 tens x 3 = 15 tens
We can add a 0 to 5 and to 15.

5**0** x 3 = 15**0**

What is the product of 500 and 3?
5 hundreds x 3 = 15 hundreds.
We can add another 0 to 5 and to 15

50**0** x 3 = 150**0**

What is the product of 4 and 5?

4 x 5 = 20

Of 40 and 5?

4**0** x 5 = 200

Of 400 and 5?

40**0** x 5 = 200**0**

Why do we have three 0's after the 2 in the product but only two 0's after the 4?

One of the 0's comes from 4 x 5.

We can multiply a number by tens or hundreds by multiplying the first digits together, then adding another 0 if one number is a ten, or two 0's if one of the numbers is a hundred.

Tell your student that we can write multiplication problems vertically.

Write
$$\begin{array}{r} 3 \\ \times \ 8 \\ \hline 24 \end{array} \qquad \begin{array}{r} 30 \\ \times \ 8 \\ \hline 240 \end{array} \qquad \begin{array}{r} 300 \\ \times \ 8 \\ \hline 2400 \end{array}$$

Show him he can first write down the 0's, and then multiply the first digit by the ones and write the product in front of the 0's. Point out that in 3 x 8, there are 24 ones, or 2 tens and 4 ones. You can draw columns and show him how all the ones are in the ones column and the tens are in the tens column. You can use notebook paper turned sideways. In 30 x 8 there are 24 tens, or 2 hundreds and 4 tens. In 300 x 8, there are 24 hundreds, or 2 thousands and 4 hundreds.

Page 49 and Learning Task 1, p. 50
Have your student rewrite the problem vertically and line up the place values carefully. Do other examples if necessary.

1. (a) 45 (b) 450 (c) 4500
   (d) 45 (e) 450 (f) 4500

Game

Material: Number cards 10, 20, 30, 40, 50, 60, 70, 80, 90, 100, 200, 300, 400, 500, 600, 700, 800, 900. A die labeled with 2, 3, 4, 5, 5, and 5.

Procedure: Shuffle the cards. Players take turns drawing one card and throwing the die. Multiply the numbers together and write the answer. After 3 turns the players add their scores. The player with the highest sum wins the round. Reshuffle cards for each round.

Workbook Exercise 21

(2) Multiplication with Renaming Only in Tens (pp. 50-51)

Multiply a 2-digit number by 2, 3, 4, or 5 with renaming only in the tens.

In this lesson, the multiplication algorithm is introduced.

Use base-10 blocks or number discs and a place value chart.

Put 42 on the chart.
Ask her to double both the tens and the ones. Ask her how many ones she has. Write 2 x 2 = 4 under the ones column of the place value chart.
Ask her how many tens she has. Write 40 x 2 = 80 under the tens column of the place value chart.
Show this on a written problem.
Tell her we usually just write the 8 for 8 tens next to the 4 in the tens column.

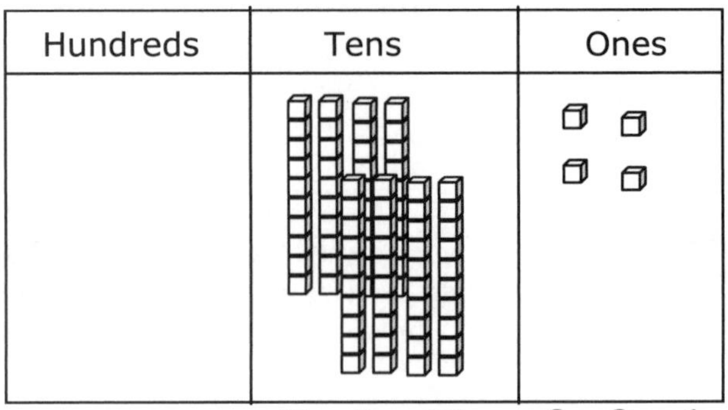

40 x 2 = 80   2 x 2 = 4

```
  42
 x 2
 ---
   4   =  2 x 2
  80   = 40 x 2
 ---
  84
```

```
  42
 x 2
 ---
  84
```

Learning Task 2, p. 50

Now do a problem where the tens are going to be renamed. She should multiply both the tens and ones on the chart before renaming. She must trade in 10 tens for 1 hundred.

```
  62                   62
 x 2                  x 2
 ---                  ---
   4   =  2 x 2       124
 120   = 60 x 2
 ---
```

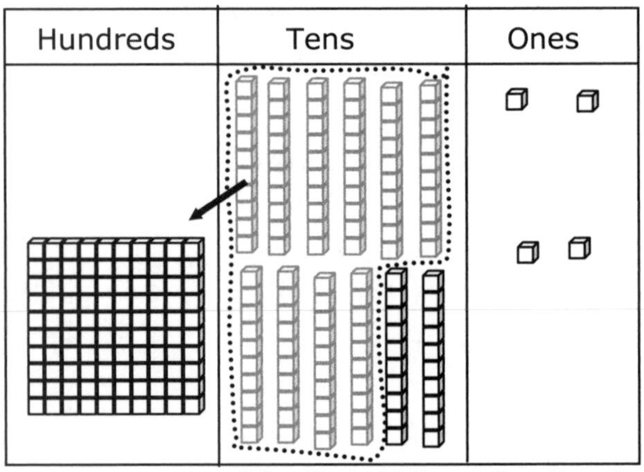

60 x 2 = 120   2 x 2 = 4

Learning Task 3. p. 51
Do other examples if necessary. Write the problem horizontally and have your student rewrite it vertically. The larger number should go on top.

Workbook Exercise 22

(3) Multiplication of a 2-Digit Number (pp. 51-52)

Multiply a 2-digit number by 2, 3, 4, or 5.

In this section, the student will have to multiply by the ones, rename the ones, multiply by the tens, and add any tens that have been renamed. Multiplication with renaming is often a difficult topic. Use concrete objects, such as base-10 blocks, extensively. Write out the steps, relating each step to the concrete example. You may want to allow your student to write the results of the multiplication below the line, and then show the "shorthand" standard method of writing the multiplication problem after your student understands the "longhand" method, as shown below.

Use **base-10 blocks** or **number discs** and a **place value chart**.

Put 56 on the chart. Have your student double the tens and ones to get twice as many. Tell him we first find the total number of ones by multiplying the ones.
6 x 2 = 12. We find the total number of tens by multiplying the tens. 50 x 2 = 100. We can then find the total. 100 + 12 = 112

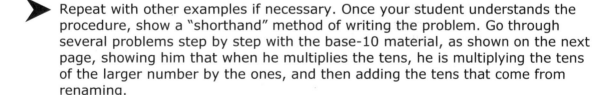

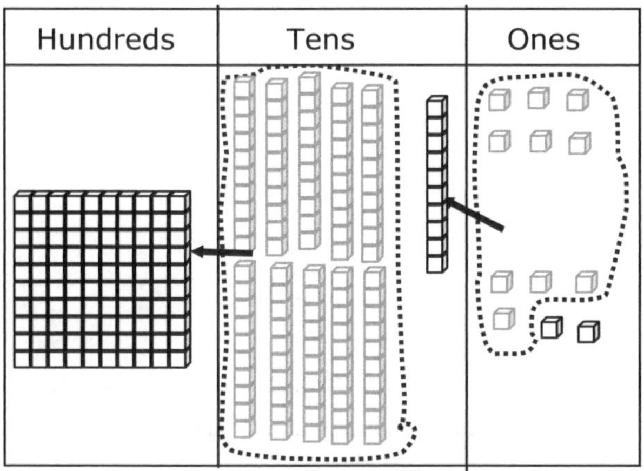

50 x 2 = 100 6 x 2 = 12
100 + 12 = 112

Write
56
x 2

Multiply the ones

56
x 2
12 **= 6 x 2**

Multiply the tens

56
x 2
12 = 6 x 2
100 **= 50 x 2**

Add

56
x 2
12 = 6 x 2
+ 100 = 50 x 2
112

Repeat with other examples if necessary. Once your student understands the procedure, show a "shorthand" method of writing the problem. Go through several problems step by step with the base-10 material, as shown on the next page, showing him that when he multiplies the tens, he is multiplying the tens of the larger number by the ones, and then adding the tens that come from renaming.

Multiply the ones. Instead of writing 32 below the line for 8 x 4, write the ones below the line, and the ten above the line. Tell him that this is to remind him to add these tens after multiplying the tens.

```
  3
 48
x 4
  2     8 x 4 = 32
```

Then multiply the tens by 4.
4 tens x 4 = 16 tens.
Remember the answer and add the 3 tens to it.
16 tens + 3 tens = 19 tens.
This can be written on the same line as he wrote the ones. Since 19 tens is 1 hundred and 9 tens, the 1 goes in the hundreds column and the 9 in the tens column.

```
  3
 48
x 4
192     8 x 4 =  30   + 2
       40 x 4 = 160
                190
                190   + 2 = 192
```

Learning Tasks 4-6, pp. 51-52
Have your student rewrite the problems vertically. Note that in (c), (f), and (i) he needs to put the larger number on top. Allow your student to use base-10 material if necessary. Do other examples if necessary.

6. (a) 162 (b) 48 (c) 111
(d) 208 (e) 92 (f) 225
(g) 189 (h) 120 (i) 152

Workbook Exercise 23

(4) Multiplication of a 3-Digit Number (p. 53)

Multiply a 3-digit number by 2, 3, 4, or 5.

The multiplication algorithm can be a difficult concept for students. Provide plenty of practice with base-10 material, illustrating each step. A suggested procedure is given. If your student has trouble with understanding the standard algorithm, you may want to first show the "longhand" written approach, where the products are written below the line and then added, and then relate that to the standard method.

Use base-10 blocks or **number discs** and a place-value chart. Place 456 on the chart, and then three times as many.

Thousands	Hundreds	Tens	Ones
	100 100 100 100	10 10 10 10 10	1 1 1 1 1 1
	100 100 100 100	10 10 10 10 10	1 1 1 1 1 1
	100 100 100 100	10 10 10 10 10	1 1 1 1 1 1

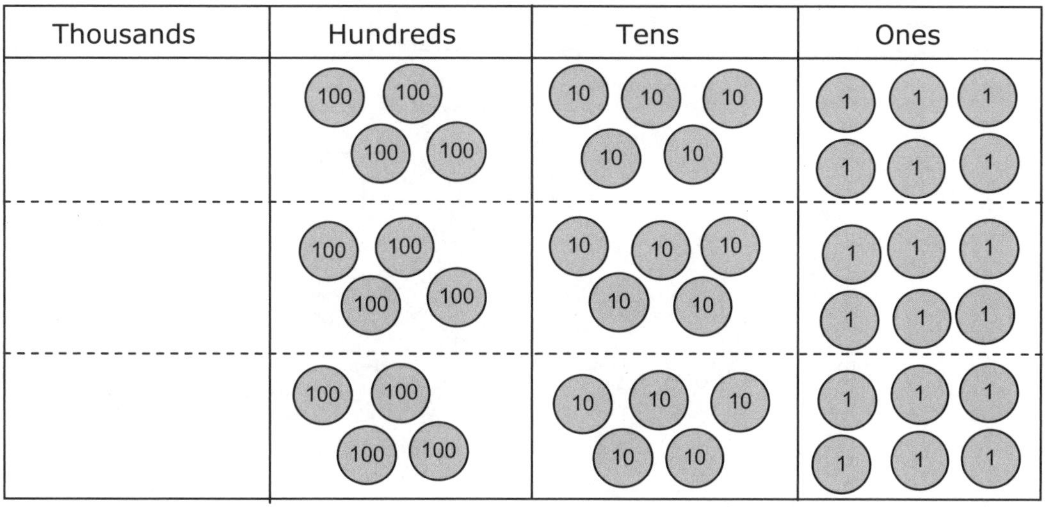

Write

$$\begin{array}{r} 456 \\ \times\ \ \ 3 \end{array}$$

Multiply 6 ones by 3 ones to find total ones. 6 x 3 = 18. There are 18 ones, or 1 ten and 8 ones. Trade 10 ones for a ten.

Thousands	Hundreds	Tens	Ones
	100 100 100 100	10 10 10 10 10 10	1 1 1 1 1 1
	100 100 100 100	10 10 10 10 10	1 1 1 1 1 1
	100 100 100 100	10 10 10 10 10	1 1 1 1 1 1

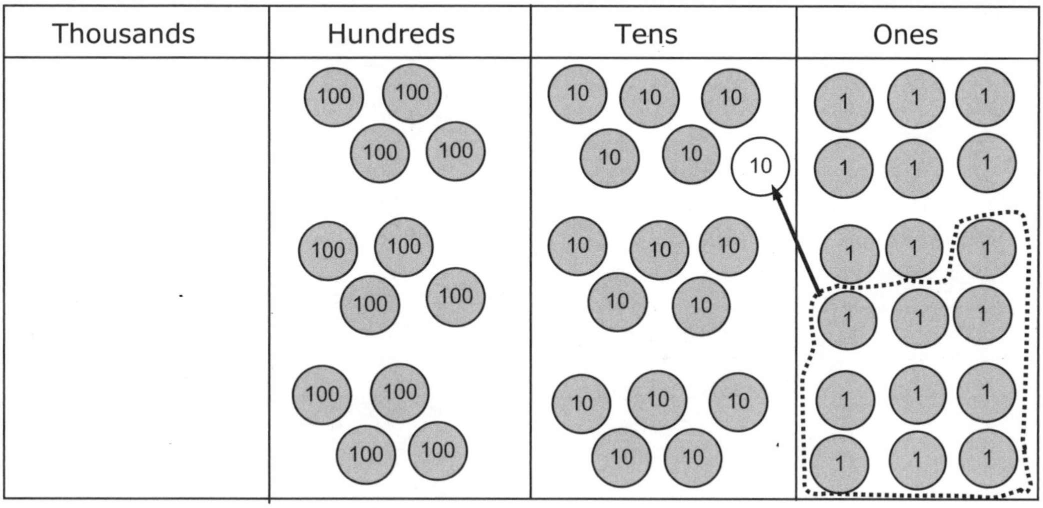

We have 1 ten and 8 ones. We write the number of tens above the tens to remind us that we have an extra ten from renaming, and we write the ones below the line. This is the final number of ones.

$$\begin{array}{r} 1 \\ 456 \\ \times\ \ \ 3 \\ \hline 8 \end{array}$$

Or write:

$$\begin{array}{r} 456 \\ \times\ \ \ 3 \\ \hline 18 \end{array} = 6 \times 3$$

Multiply the 5 tens by 3 ones to find the total tens. 50 x 3 = 150. This gives 15 tens, or 1 hundred and 5 tens. Trade 10 tens for a hundred.

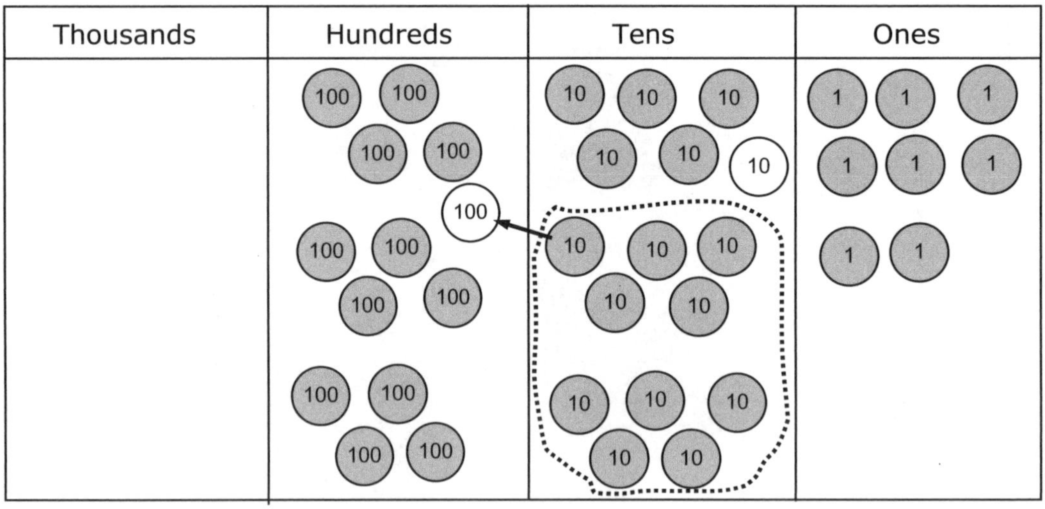

We need to write the total number of tens. We have the tens from multiplying 5 tens by 3 ones, which is 15 tens, and we have the ten from renaming the ones. We add that to the 15 tens, which gives 16 tens. This is 1 hundred and 6 tens.

We write the hundred over the hundreds to remind us to add it later, and write the tens below the line. This is the final number of tens.

```
 11
 456
x  3
  68
```

Or write:

```
  456
x   3
   18   = 6 x 3
 +150   = 50 x 3
  168
```

Multiply the 4 hundreds by 3 ones to find the total hundreds. 400 x 3 = 1200. This gives 12 hundreds, or one thousand and 2 hundreds. Trade 10 hundreds for a thousand.

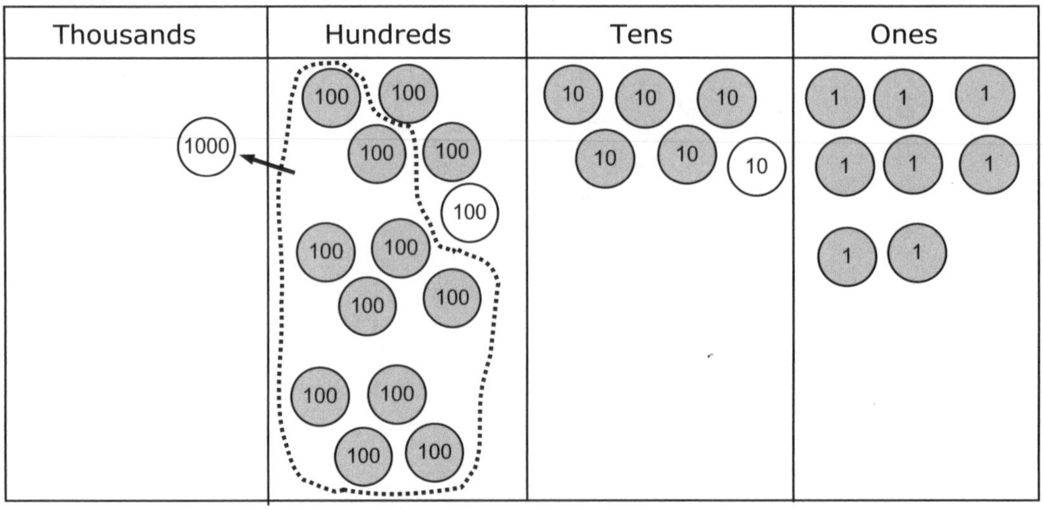

We need to write the total number of hundreds. We have the hundreds from multiplying 4 hundreds by 3 ones, which is 12 hundreds, and we have 1 hundred from renaming the tens. We add that to the 12 hundreds, which gives 13 hundreds. This is 1 thousand and 3 hundreds. We have no more multiplications to do, so we write the thousands in the thousands column, and the hundreds in the hundreds column.

```
  11
 456
x  3
----
1368
```

Or write:

```
  456
x   3
-----
   18   = 6  x 3
+ 150   = 50 x 3
-----
  168
+1200   = 400 x 3
-----
 1368   add
```

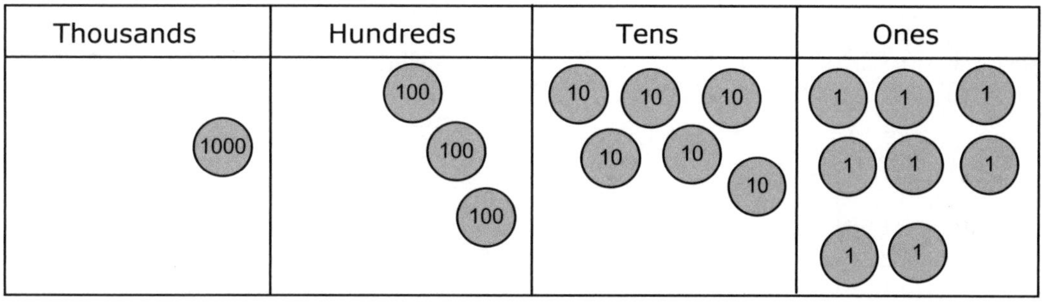

Learning Tasks 7-9, pp. 53
Allow your student to use base-10 material if necessary. Provide additional problems if necessary.

9. (a) 428 (b) 969 (c) 924
(d) 1860 (e) 902 (f) 702
(g) 867 (h) 3520 (i) 2180

Workbook Exercise 24

Part 4 Quotient and Remainder

(1) Quotient and Remainder (pp. 57-60)

Divide a 2-digit number by 2.
Understand the terms **quotient** and **remainder**.
Identify odd and even numbers.

This section introduces the division algorithm through division by 2. The division algorithm can be a difficult concept so spend adequate time explaining it thoroughly step by step.

- Arrange 24 **blocks** in an array with 4 rows and 6 columns. Write the equation

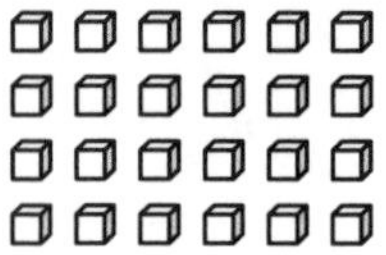

$$24 \div 4 = 6$$

Ask you student what we call the answer when we add two numbers (sum), when we subtract two numbers (difference) and when we multiply two numbers (product). Tell her there is also a special name when we divide two numbers. The answer is called the **quotient**. Ask her for the quotient in the problem you wrote.

- Tell your student that we can write the same problem in a different way. Illustrate this with the blocks by drawing a line above them and a curved line on the left side:

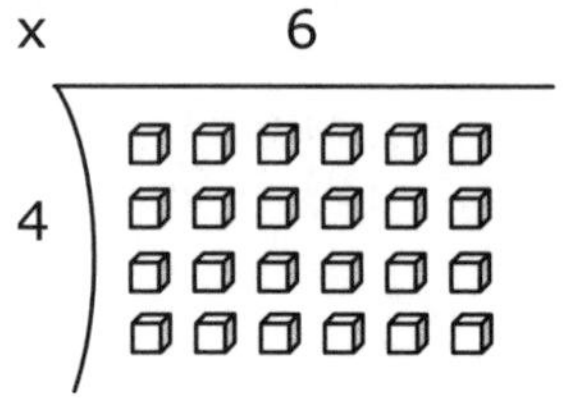

The total goes inside the "box." We only draw the box with the top and the left side. The number of groups we are dividing into goes on the left side, as if they were the number of rows. The number that goes in each group goes above the line. The number on the left side times the number on top will give the number in the "box." You can draw a little "x" in the upper left corner. Tell her that we line up place value columns for the number in the box and above the box. The 6 of the quotient goes in the ones column.

$$\begin{array}{r} 6 \\ 4\overline{)24} \end{array}$$

Write some other division problem and have her rewrite them the new way.

For example: $45 \div 5 = 9$ $\quad \begin{array}{r} 9 \\ 5\overline{)45} \end{array}$

- Use **small objects** such as base-10 cubes or linking cubes, and bowls or draw circles on a white board. Give your student 23 cubes and have her divide them equally into 3 groups by placing them in the bowls or circles. Tell her the number left over is called the remainder. Write an equation for what she did. For example, if you gave her 23 cubes and she divided them up into 3 groups, you would write

$$23 \div 3 = 7 \text{ with a remainder of } 2$$

Tell her we can write "with a remainder" as "R" or "r."

$$23 \div 3 = 7 \text{ R } 2$$

Write step by step as you explain:

$$\begin{array}{rl} 7 \text{ R } 2 & \\ 3\overline{)23} & \\ \underline{21} & = 3 \times 7 \\ 2 & = 23 - 21 \end{array}$$

Tell your student that we write the number of cubes that we can share evenly below the total in the "box." We need to line up the tens and ones. We can subtract that from the total to get the number left over, or the remainder. We write it like a subtraction problem written vertically.

- Use **base-10 blocks**. Set out a ten and 5 ones. Draw two circles or use 2 bowls. Write

$$15 \div 2$$

Your student will probably know that the answer is 7 with a remainder of 1. Ask him how we can divide the ten. We need to rename it as ones. Replace the ten with 10 ones. Tell him that there are now 15 ones and ask him to divide them into the two circles. There is a remainder of 1. Write, explaining the steps:

$$15 \div 2 = 7 \text{ R } 1$$

$$\begin{array}{r} 7 \text{ R } 1 \\ 2\overline{)15} \\ \underline{14} \\ 1 \end{array}$$

Tell him he needs to think of a number closest to 15 that can be evenly divided by 2. That would be 14. $14 \div 2 = 7$. 7 is the quotient, or how many each group gets, and goes above the line. That number times 2 is how many were put evenly into the bowls and that goes below the 15. Then we subtract to get the remainder.

➤ Set out 5 tens and 7 ones. Draw 2 circles. Write the division problem
Tell your student that first we divide up the tens. We can put two tens in each circle. We write the number that goes in each group above the line. These are tens, so they go in the tens column. We write the total number of tens that we have "handed out" underneath, and since they are tens, we put it in the tens column. We subtract to find the number of tens left over.

$$2\overline{)57}$$

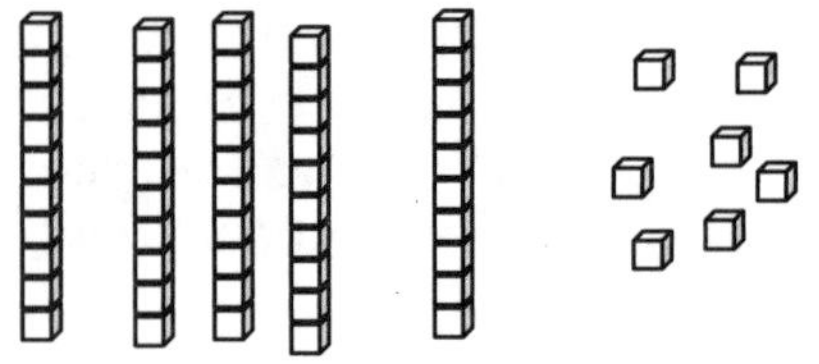

$$\begin{array}{r} 2 \\ 2\overline{)57} \\ 4 \\ \hline 1 \end{array}$$

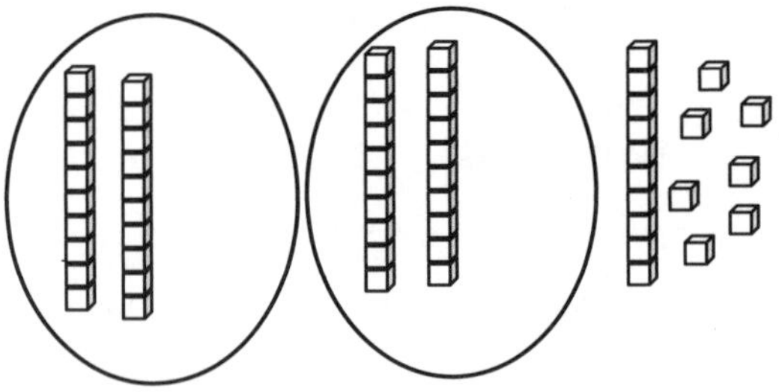

In order to divide up the ten, we need to trade it in for ones. So we have 17 ones left over.

$$\begin{array}{r} 2 \\ 2\overline{)57} \\ 4 \\ \hline 17 \end{array}$$

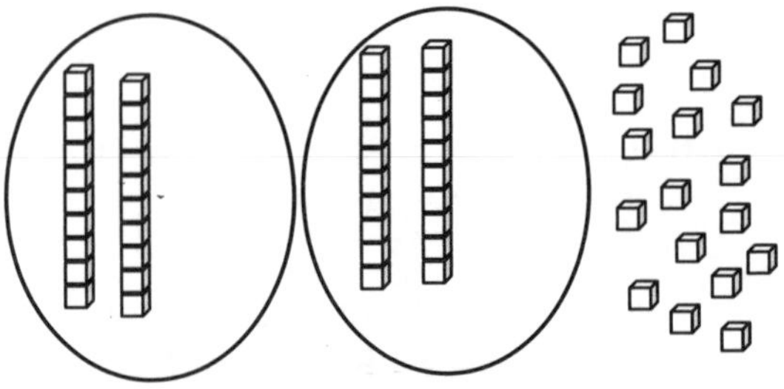

Now we divide up the ones into the two groups. Each group gets 8. This number goes above the line. It is the number of ones, so it goes in the ones column.
8 x 2 = 16
We write the total "handed out" underneath and subtract to get the remainder.

$$\begin{array}{r} 28 \\ 2\overline{)57} \\ 4 \\ \hline 17 \\ 16 \\ \hline 1 \end{array}$$

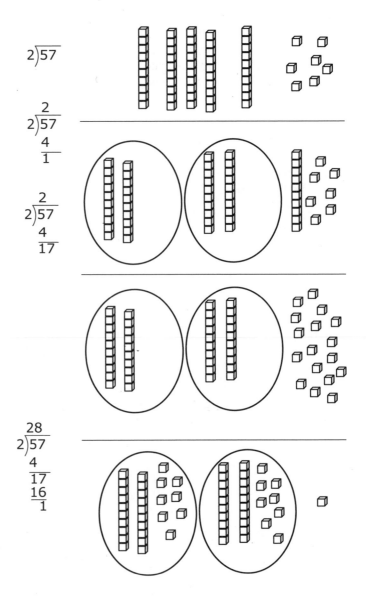

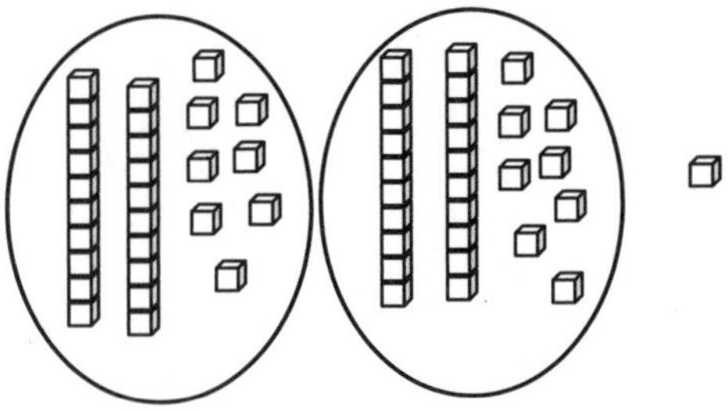

Repeat, step by step, with another number divided by 2, this time one where there is no remainder, such as 68 ÷ 2.

➤ Ask your student for all possible remainders for a number divided by 2. The only possible remainder is 1. Tell him that if the remainder is 1, the number is called an **odd** number. If there is no remainder, the number is called an **even** number.

- Use a **100-chart**. Have your student circle the numbers he lands on when he counts by twos. Ask him what the remainder would be if these numbers were divided by 2. There would be no remainder. These are even numbers. Ask him if he sees a pattern. All even numbers end with 2, 4, 6, 8, or 0. All odd numbers end with 1, 3, 5, 7, or 9.

- Ask your student: Is 0 odd or even?
  If we divide it by 2, each group would get 0, and there would be no remainder. So 0 is even.

Pages 57-58 and Learning Tasks 1-6 pp. 58-60
In the learning tasks, relate what is happening in the pictures with the division algorithm. Illustrate with concrete base-10 material if necessary. Make sure your student thoroughly understands the division algorithm when dividing by 2. For example, in learning task 4, there are 3 tens. Two of them get put into the 2 groups, one in each group. One ten is the remainder and is renamed as ones. The ones are then put into the two groups. Show how the number that goes in each group is written above the line in the right place value, and the total number put in the groups is written below and subtracted to get the remainder.

Workbook Exercise 25
Workbook Review 2
Workbook Review 3

Enrichment 4
Magic Squares

A magic square is an array of numbers that is arranged such that

- There are the same number of rows and columns.
- No number is used more than once.
- The sum of every row, column, and each of the two diagonals is the same number, called the **magic sum**.
- The basic magic square is formed using consecutive numbers beginning with the number 1, but squares can be adapted by changing the order of the numbers, by adding a constant to all numbers, or by using multiples of the basic number sequence.

Here is a magic square. We will call each smaller square within the square a cell. What is the magic sum? Divide each number by 2 and put it in the corresponding cell in the square next to it. One is done for you. Is the new square a magic square? What is its magic sum?

32	72	16
24	40	56
64	8	48

	4	

Here is a common procedure for constructing a magic square with an odd number of cells, such as 9. You can begin with any number. We will begin with 1. Put the number 1 in the center top cell. Put the next number, 2, one cell above and one cell to the right of the previous number. If this puts it outside the square, put it in the cell that is in the same column but in the bottom (as with 2) or in the same row but in the left column (as with 3).

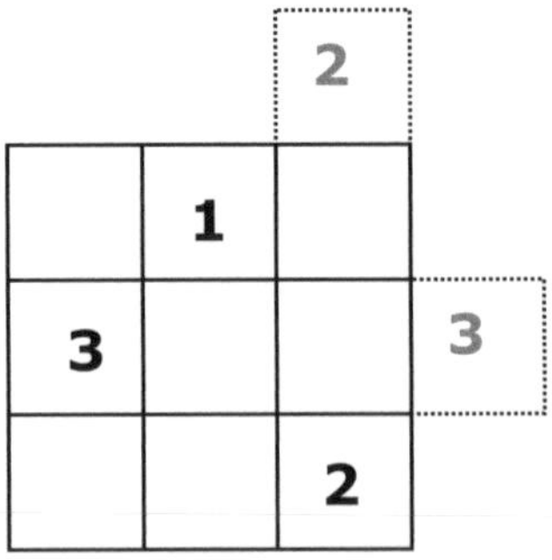

If a number can't be put in a cell because it already has a number, put it in the cell directly below the previous cell. 4 would go in the cell that already has 1, so it goes below the 3. 5 and 6 are put in cells up one and to the right one. 7 would fall outside the square, and should go in the cell occupied by 4, so put it below the 6. 8 would go outside the square, in the top row, so put it in the top row of the left column. 9 would also go outside the square in the middle column, so put it in the middle column at the bottom.

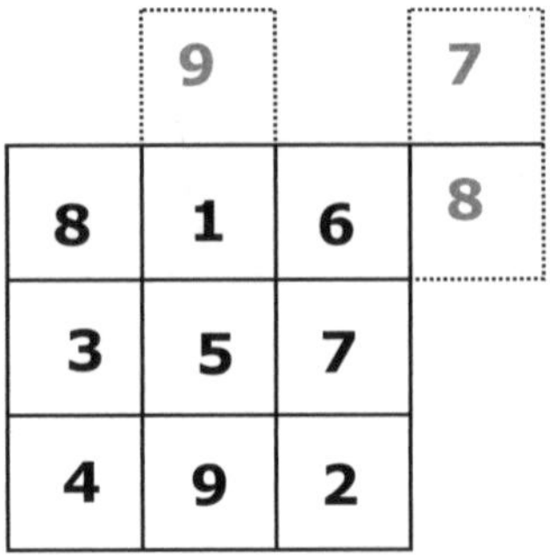

What is the magic sum of this square?

See if you can follow the rules for placing numbers starting with 12

If you do it correctly, the magic sum will be 48.

	12	

		1		
				3
		25	2	

Then try one with 25 squares, starting with 1. The first three numbers and the last one have been placed for you. If you do it correctly the magic sum will be 65.

Now, multiply each number by 5 and put it in the corresponding cell of this square. What is the new magic sum?

		5		
				15
		125	10	

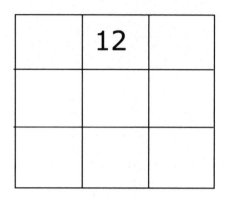

Part 5 Dividing Hundreds, Tens and Ones

(1) Dividing 2-Digit Numbers by 2, 3, 4, and 5 (pp. 61-63)

Divide a 2-digit number by 3, 4 or 5.

➤ Use **base-10 blocks** and help your student perform division of 2-digit numbers by 3, 4, or 5. Remind her to first "hand out" or divide the tens into equal groups, write the number each group gets above the line in the tens place, and the number "handed out" below the tens to find the remainder. Then the remaining tens need to be renamed as ones, combined with the ones already there, and then all the ones need to be divided into groups. The number each group gets again goes above the line, this time in the ones place, and the number "handed out" goes below to subtract it from the total ones, giving the remainder.

Do some without base-10 blocks. Remind her that in order to determine how many each group gets, she needs to think of the number closest to the tens or the ones she needs to divide that is a multiple of the number of groups. For example, in 80 ÷ 3, she needs to first divide the tens. 6 is the closest multiple of 3 to 8. 3 x ? = 6. ? = 2, so two tens would be put in each group, 6 tens total.

➤ Use a **100-chart**. Have your student circle all the multiples of 3 by counting by threes. Ask her what the remainder would be if these numbers were divided by 3. It would be 0. Pick several numbers right after a multiple of 3 and ask what the remainder would be if those numbers were divided by 3. Repeat with some numbers two more than a multiple of 3. Ask her for the possible remainders for any number divided by 3. The remainder of any number divided by 3 is 0, 1 or 2.

Look at the circled numbers again. Ask her to add the digits together, and then add the digits of the sum together if the answer is more than one digit. For example, for 39, the sum of the digits is 12, and the sum of those digits is 3. Do it with several numbers until she sees a pattern. A number where the sum of the digits is 3, 6, or 9 will have no remainders when divided by 3.

Erase the circles, or use a new chart, and now have your student circle all the numbers she lands on when counting by fours. See if she can figure out all possible remainders for any number divided by 4. The remainder of any number divided by 4 is 0, 1, 2, or 3. Now have her look at the numbers to see if she sees a pattern. All the numbers are even numbers. Note that all even numbers can't be divided by 4 without a remainder.

Repeat with multiples of 5. The remainder of any number divided by 5 is 0, 1, 2, 3, or 4. All numbers that end in 0 or 5 will have no remainders when divided by 5.

➤ Give your student the following problem:

> Joe has some pennies. The total number of pennies is less than 50. When he puts them in piles of 2, he has 1 left over. When he puts them in piles of 3, he has 2 left over. When he puts them in piles of 4, he has 3 left over. When he puts them in piles of 5, he has none left over. How many pennies does he have?

Since there is 1 left over when he puts them in piles of 2, the number is odd. Since there are none left over when he puts them in piles of 5, he must have 5, 15, 25, 35, or 45 pennies. 15 and 45 give a remainder of 0 when he puts them in piles of 3, so it can't be those numbers. 25 has a remainder of 1 when divided by 3, so it can't be that number. That leaves 5 and 35. 5 can be put in one pile of 4, but the remainder is 1. 35 divided by 4 gives a remainder of 3. So he has 35 pennies.

Learning Tasks 1-3, p. 63

3. (a) 24 (b) 20 (c) 18
   (d) 12 r3 (e) 15 (f) 13 r2

Game

Material: Use a **die** and deck of **playing cards** with tens and face cards removed and the 1 of each ten covered up, making them 0. Divide the cards into black cards and red cards.

Procedure: Shuffle and deal out the black and red cards separately so each player has a face-down pile of red cards and of black cards. Each player turns over one red and one black card and throws the die. The red card is the tens, the black card is the ones. The player divides his number by the number on the die. The person with the highest quotient without the remainder gets the cards. If two players have the same quotient, the one with the highest remainder gets the cards. Rolling a six can be counted as losing the round, or the six can be covered up and replaced with a number with which the student needs the most practice.

Workbook Exercise 26

(2) Dividing 3-Digit Numbers by 2, 3, 4, and 5 (p. 64)

Divide a 3-digit number by 3, 4 or 5.

Use **base-10 blocks** and help your student perform division of 3-digit numbers by 3, 4, or 5. Tell him that the procedure is the same as with 2-digit numbers, except that now he first has to divide the hundreds. Any remainders from dividing hundreds get renamed as tens, and are added to the tens already there, then the tens are divided up, as before.

Start with division of a 3-digit number by 2. You can follow a procedure similar to that on pages 61-62 of the text. Start with four hundreds. They can be divided evenly; there are no remainders, so the answer is 200.

Then do 500. Each group gets 2 of them, so 2 goes above the line in the hundreds place because it is two hundreds. There will be a hundred left over, which has to be renamed as tens, and each group gets 5 tens. There are none left over, all have been "handed out" or divided up, so no one gets a one. Put 0 for no ones. Each group got 250.

```
   250
2)500
  4
  10
  10
   0
```

Now do 550 ÷ 2. This time the hundred that is left over is added to the 5 tens, giving 15 tens, and each group gets 7 tens, leaving 1 which needs to be renamed as ones and divided up. Each group gets 5 of them.

```
   275
2)550
  4
  15
  14
   10
   10
    0
```

Do a problem in which there are not enough tens to divide, such as 810 ÷ 2. Since no tens go into the groups, a 0 has to be written in the tens place above the line. Note that there are no remainders with the hundreds.

```
   405
2)810
  8
   10
   10
    0
```

Learning Tasks 4-6, p. 64.
Allow your student to work these out with base-10 blocks if necessary.

6. (a) 88 (b) 320 (c) 86 r3
   (d) 233 r1 (e) 72 r2 (f) 35
   (g) 62 r1 (h) 187 (i) 102 r1

Workbook Exercise 27

Unit 4 Multiplication Tables of 6, 7, 8 and 9

Part 1 Looking Back

(1) Looking Back (pp. 68-69)

Understand doubles and square numbers

Pages 68-69
Tell your student that she knows all of the facts in the lighter color on this page, and now she is going to learn the 16 darker colored ones.

➤ Use a filled-in **multiplication chart**, such as the one in Mental Math 17, to discuss doubles. If she has not already filled it in, have her do so now. She can obtain any facts she does not know by repeated addition. Discuss doubles by looking at the rows.

Point to the row for x 2. These are all doubles of the numbers in the top row. Now, point to the row for x 4. Ask: For what row are these doubles? (The x 2 row.) The numbers in the x 8 row are doubles of the numbers in which row? (The x 4 row.) Do you see any other rows where the numbers are doubles of the numbers in another row? (x 6 is double x 3, x 10 is double x 5.)

Have her practice mentally doubling two-digit numbers up through 50 without the chart. She can double the tens, double the ones, and then add the products together.

48 x 2 = double 40 + double 8 = (40 x 2) + (8 x 2) = 80 + 16 = 76
36 x 2 = double 30 + double 6 = 60 + 12 = 72

Try continuous doubling:

2, 4, 8, 16, 32, 64
3, 6, 12, 24, 48, 96

➤ Use the **multiplication chart** to teach square numbers.

Circle all the numbers along the diagonal. These numbers are called **square** numbers. They fall at the lower right of a square with the same number of rows and columns. A square number is the product of two numbers which are the same.

➤ List the square numbers:

1 x 1 = 1
2 x 2 = 4
3 x 3 = 9
4 x 4 = 16
5 x 5 = 25
6 x 6 = 36
7 x 7 = 49
8 x 8 = 64
9 x 9 = 81
10 x 10 = 100

Your student should know the squares of 1 to 5 and 10. Do not require that she memorize the squares of 6, 7, 8, and 9 yet.

Workbook Exercise 28
Your student may have already done this exercise. If so, just move on to the next section.

Enrichment 5
Mental Multiplication

Multiplication of a 2-digit number by a 1-digit number can be done mentally by first multiplying the tens, then the ones, and adding the two products together:

52 x 4	50	+	2	
	x		4	
	200	+	8	= 208
47 x 3	40	+	7	
	x		3	
	120	+	21	= 141
39 x 5	30	+	9	
	x		5	
	150	+	45	= 195

Go through these examples with your student, illustrating with base-10 blocks if necessary. Do other examples if necessary. Only do multiplication by 2, 3, 4, or 5 for now. Mental Math 18 has further practice.

Part 2 Multiplying and Dividing by 6

(1) Multiplying by 6 (pp. 70-72)

Obtain multiplication facts of 6 based on other facts.
Memorize multiplication facts for 6.

You may want to use **linking cubes** in sets of 6. Set out 10 rows. Have your student write all the multiplication facts.

1 x 6 = 6	6 x 1 = 6
2 x 6 = 12	6 x 2 = 12
3 x 6 = 18	6 x 3 = 18
4 x 6 = 24	6 x 4 = 24
5 x 6 = 30	6 x 5 = 30
6 x 6 = 36	**6 x 6 = 36**
7 x 6 = 42	**6 x 7 = 42**
8 x 6 = 48	**6 x 8 = 48**
9 x 6 = 54	**6 x 9 = 54**
10 x 6 = 60	6 x 10 = 60

Point out that he already knows all except for four of the multiplication facts for 6.

Learning Task 3, p. 73

Learning Tasks 1-2(a), p. 71

A new multiplication fact can be obtained from known facts.
We know that 6 x 5 equals 30.
6 x 6 is 6 more, or 36.

Learning Task 2(b), p. 72

Multiplication by 6 can be split into two products.
6 x 7 can be split into 6 x 5 and 6 x 2.
To get 6 x 7, add their products.
6 x 7 = 30 + 12 = 42
Have your student split 6 x 7 and 6 x 8 into two products that he knows.

Learning Task 2(c), p. 72
The product of a number and 8 can be done by doubling the number three times.
6 x 8 = double double double 6 = double double 12 = double 24 = 48
Think: 6, 12, 24, 48

Learning Task 2(d), p. 72

The product of a number and 9 can obtained from the fact for x 10.
We know that 6 x 10 equals 60.
6 x 9 is 6 less, or 54.

➤ You may also want to help your student see that multiplication by 6 can be done by doubling multiplication by 3.
6 x 6 = double 6 x 3 = double 18 = 36
6 x 7 = double 7 x 3 = double 21 = 42
6 x 8 = double 8 x 3 = double 24 = 48
6 x 9 = double 9 x 3 = double 27 = 54

Your student can use any of these methods until he has the facts memorized.

War

Material: **Playing cards** with the face cards removed, **or** four sets **of number cards** 1-10. **Dice**.

Procedure: Shuffle the cards and deal all out. Leave the cards face down in a pile in front of each player. Each player throws a dice and turns over a card and multiplies the card number by the dice number. The player with the largest product gets all the cards. If two players have the same product, the one with the highest card gets the cards. The winner is the one with the most cards after all the cards are turned over.

Variation: Use 2 decks of cards. Use only the black cards ace through 10 from one deck. Use all the red cards ace through 6 and the 10s from the same deck. Use the red cards 3, 4, and 6 from the second deck. Make 2 sets from these cards, one of black cards only and one of red cards only. Deal out the cards separately so that each player has a pile of black cards and a pile of red cards. Each player turns over one card from each pile and multiplies the numbers together. The player with the largest product gets all the cards. The winner is the one with the most cards after all the cards are turned over.

Workbook Exercise 29

(2) Dividing 6 (p. 73)

Memorize the division facts for 6.

Remind your student, if necessary, that division facts are related to multiplication facts.

To find the answer to 48 ÷ 6, we can think of the number times 6 that gives 48

48 ÷ 6 = ____ ____ x 6 = 48 $48 \underset{\times 6}{\overset{\div 6}{\rightleftarrows}} 8$

For division by 6, We can also find half the number, and then divide by 3:

Half of 48 is 24, 24 ÷ 3 = 8, so 48 ÷ 6 = 8

Learning Task 4, p. 73

4. 5 7 8 9

Concentration

Material: **Index cards** with the division fact on some and the answers on others. There should be 20 cards, 10 with a division such as 36 ÷ 6 and 10 with the answers.

Procedure: Shuffle the cards and place in a 4 x 5 array. The players take turns turning over two cards in place. If one card has the answer to the other card, the player gets the card. If not, the cards are turned back face down. The winner is the one with the most cards after all cards have been matched.

Beat the clock (single player)

Material: **Index cards** with the facts on some and the answers on others, and a **timer**. Use facts that the student is having the most trouble remembering.

Procedure: Place the answer cards face up on the table. Shuffle the fact cards. Start the timer. The player turns over one card at a time and matches it with a card on the table. His score is the amount of time it takes to match all the cards. Play again and see if a lower score can be achieved.

Workbook Exercise 30

(3) Multiplication Algorithm with 6 (p. 74)

Multiply 2 and 3 digit numbers by 6.

Your student should be able to recall facts for 6. If necessary, have her continue practicing them with fact practice or games. Review the steps for the multiplication algorithm using the examples in the text.

Learning Task 5-6, p. 74

6. (a) 204 (b) 342 (c) 414
   (d) 648 (e) 2832 (f) 5460

Workbook Exercise 31

(4) Division Algorithm with 6 (p. 74)

Divide 2 and 3 digit numbers by 6.

Your student should be able to recall the division facts for 6. If necessary, have him continue practicing them with fact practice or games if necessary.

Use a **hundreds-chart**. Circle all the multiples of 6. Ask the following: How will you find the multiples after 6 x 9? (Count by 6.) What is the remainder when these numbers are divided by 6? (0) Are the numbers you circled odd or even? (Even) Add the digits of these numbers together. If the sum had two digits, add the digits together again. (e.g. 84: 8 + 4 = 12, 1 + 2 = 3). Do you see a pattern? (The sum of the digits are be 3, 6, or 9.) What pattern does this remind you of? (Numbers that can be divided evenly by 3.) So numbers that are divisible by 6 without a remainder are also divisible by 3, and are even. What are all the possible remainders when a number is divided by 6? (0, 1, 2, 3, 4, or 5)

Review the steps for the division algorithm using the examples in the text.

Learning Tasks 7-8, p. 74
Allow your student to use base-10 blocks, if necessary.

8. (a) 16 (b) 14 r5 (c) 12 r3
(d) 57 (e) 118 (f) 102 r3

Workbook Exercises 32-33

Part 3 Multiplying and Dividing by 7

(1) Multiplying and Dividing by 7 (pp. 76-79)

Obtain multiplication facts for 7 based on other facts.
Memorize the multiplication facts for 7.
Memorize the division facts for 7.

Use **linking cubes** in sets of 7. Set out 10 rows and write or have your student write all the multiplication facts and the related division facts.

1 x 7 = 7	7 x 1 = 7	7 ÷ 7 = 1
2 x 7 = 14	7 x 2 = 14	14 ÷ 7 = 2
3 x 7 = 21	7 x 3 = 21	21 ÷ 7 = 3
4 x 7 = 28	7 x 4 = 28	28 ÷ 7 = 4
5 x 7 = 35	7 x 5 = 35	35 ÷ 7 = 5
6 x 7 = 42	7 x 6 = 42	42 ÷ 7 = 6
7 x 7 = 49	**7 x 7 = 49**	49 ÷ 7 = 7
8 x 7 = 56	**7 x 8 = 56**	56 ÷ 7 = 8
9 x 7 = 63	**7 x 9 = 63**	63 ÷ 7 = 9
10 x 7 = 70	6 x 10 = 70	70 ÷ 7 = 10

Point out that there are only three new multiplication facts to learn.

Learning Task 4, p. 79, page 76

Learning Tasks 1-2(a), p. 77

A new multiplication fact can be obtained from known facts.
We know that 7 x 5 = 35.
7 x 6 is 6 more, or 42.

Learning Task 2(b), p. 77

Multiplication by 7 can be split into two products.
7 x 7 can be split into 7 x 5 and 7 x 2.
7 x 7 can be obtained by adding those products.
7 x 7 = = 35 + 14 = 49.

Have your student split 7 x 8 and 7 x 9 into two products that he knows.

Learning Task 2(c), p. 77

The product of a number and 8 can be done by doubling the number three times.
7 x 8 = double double double 7 = double double 14 = double 28 = 56
Think: 7, 14, 28, 56

Learning Task 2(d), p. 77

Multiplying by 9 can be done by starting with multiplication by 10.
If we know 7 x 10 = 70, then 7 x 9 is 7 less, or 63.

War

Material: Two decks **Playing cards.** Use only the black cards ace through 10 from one deck. Use all the red cards ace through 7 and the 10s from the same deck. Use the red cards 4, 6, and 7 from the second deck.

Procedure: Shuffle the cards separately and deal them all out so that each player has a pile of black cards and a pile of red cards. Each player turns over one card from each pile and multiplies the numbers together. The player with the largest product gets all the cards that have been turned over. If two players have the same product the one with the highest number on the card (factor) gets the cards. The winner is the one with the most cards after all the cards are turned over.

Learning Tasks 3 and 5, pp. 78-79

3. 14 28 70
5. (a) 42 (b) 49 (c) 63
(d) 8 (e) 10 (f) 3

Workbook Exercise 34

(2) Multiplication Algorithm with 7 (p. 79)

Multiply 2 and 3 digit numbers by 7.

Your student should be able to recall the multiplication facts for 7. Have her continue practicing them with fact practice or games if necessary.

Learning Task 6, p. 79

6.	(a) 392	(b) 441	(c) 497
	(d) 6440	(e) 5628	(f) 1526

Workbook Exercise 35

(3) Division Algorithm with 7 (p. 79)

Divide 2 and 3 digit numbers by 7.

Your student should be able to recall division facts of 7. Have her continue practicing them with fact practice or games if necessary.

Ask your student for the possible remainders for a number divided by 7. They are 0, 1, 2, 3, 4, 5, and 6. Ask her why she would never get a remainder of 7. If she had 7 left, she could divide them, one into each group.

Learning Tasks 7-8, p. 79

7.	(a) 10 r5	(b) 12	(c) 9 r1
	(d) 13	(e) 14	(f) 11 r3
8.	(a) 15 r3	(b) 33	(c) 97 r3
	(d) 104 r2	(e) 136 r2	(f) 100 r5

Workbook Exercises 36-37
Workbook Review 4

Part 4 Multiplying and Dividing by 8

(1) Multiplying and Dividing by 8 (pp. 82-83)

Obtain multiplication facts for 8 based on other facts.
Memorize multiplication facts for 8.
Memorize facts for division by 8.

➤ Use a completed **multiplication chart**, such as the one for Mental Math 10. Draw your student's attention to the row for x 2, then x 4, then x 8.

Remind her that the numbers in the x 4 row are double those in the x 2 row above, and the numbers in the x 8 row are double those in the x 4 row above.

To find a number times 8, we can double it three times.

8 x 8 = double double double 8 = double double 16 = double 32 = 64

Division by 8 can be done by halving, or dividing by 2, three times. If she remembers her division facts for 4, she can divide by 2 once, then divide the quotient by 4.

➤ There are only two new facts, 8 x 8 and 9 x 8 here. Spend some time helping your student learn the facts, particularly the division facts, through fact practice and games such as those suggested in earlier sections of this guide.

Page 82 and Learning Tasks 1-3

1. 6 10 12
   32 64

2. (a) 24 (b) 40 (c) 64
   (d) 32 (e) 56 (f) 72

3. (a) 10 (b) 6 (c) 3
   (d) 9 (e) 7 (f) 5

Workbook Exercise 38

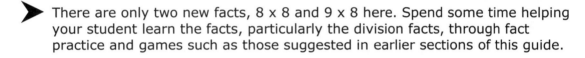

(2) Multiplication Algorithm with 8 (p. 83)

Multiply 2 and 3 digit numbers by 8.

➤ Your student should be able to recall or quickly obtain the multiplication facts for 8. Continue with fact practice or games if necessary.

Learning Task 4, p. 83
Provide additional problems if necessary.

4.	(a) 448	(b) 632	(c) 544
	(d) 3344	(e) 2440	(f) 4960

Workbook Exercise 39

(3) Division Algorithm with 8 (p. 83)

Divide 2 and 3 digit numbers by 8.

➤ Your student should know the division facts for 8. Continue with fact practice or games if necessary.

➤ Ask your student for the possible remainders for a number divided by 8. They are 0, 1, 2, 3, 4, 5, 6, and 7.

Learning Task 5, p. 83
Provide additional problems if necessary.

5.	(a) 12 r2	(b) 14	(c) 100 r7
	(d) 38 r1	(e) 83	(f) 120

Workbook Exercises 40-41

Part 5 Multiplying and Dividing by 9

(1) Multiplying and Dividing by 9 (pp. 86-88)

Obtain multiplication facts of 9 based on other facts.
Memorize multiplication facts for 9.
Memorize division facts for 9.

There is only one new multiplication fact to learn; 9 x 9.

Use a **hundreds-chart**. Circle multiples of 9 by counting by 9's. Ask: Do you see any patterns? (The circled numbers are one row below and one column to the left of the previous number.) We can add 9 to a number by adding 10 (down one row) and subtracting 1 (to the left one column.

Write the facts for 9:

1 x 9 = 9
2 x 9 = 18
3 x 9 = 27
4 x 9 = 36
5 x 9 = 45
6 x 9 = 54
7 x 9 = 63
8 x 9 = 72
9 x 9 = 81
10 x 9 = 90

Ask: Do you see a pattern? Look at the tens and the ones. The tens increase by 1, and the ones decrease by 1. Find the sum of the digits of the product. What is the sum? (9) Look at the tens digit and compare it to the number that is being multiplied by 9. (It is one less.) So the tens digit of a number multiplied by 9 is one less than the number, and the ones digit is the difference between the value of the tens digit and 9.

Page 86
We can obtain the x 9 facts from the x 10 facts.

$1 \xrightarrow{\times 10} 10 \xrightarrow{-1} 9$

$2 \xrightarrow{\times 10} 20 \xrightarrow{-2} 18$

$3 \xrightarrow{\times 10} 30 \xrightarrow{-3} 27$

$4 \xrightarrow{\times 10} 40 \xrightarrow{-4} 36$

$5 \xrightarrow{\times 10} 50 \xrightarrow{-5} 45$

$6 \xrightarrow{\times 10} 60 \xrightarrow{-6} 54$

$7 \xrightarrow{\times 10} 70 \xrightarrow{-7} 63$

$8 \xrightarrow{\times 10} 80 \xrightarrow{-8} 72$

$9 \xrightarrow{\times 10} 90 \xrightarrow{-9} 81$

Learning Task 1, p. 87
The sum of the digits is always 9.

Learning Task 2, p. 87
Show your student that she can hold up both hands in front of her and put down the finger for the number being multiplied by 9. The number of fingers to the left of the bent finger will be the tens digit, and the number of fingers to the right will be the ones digit.

Learning Task 3, p. 88
We can obtain the x 9 facts from other facts.
In (a), 9 times an even number is 18 times half that number.
In (b), 9 times 6 is double 9 times 3. 9 times a number can also be obtained by multiplying that number by 3 twice.

Learning Tasks 4-5, p. 88

4.	(a) 18	(b) 36	(c) 27
	(d) 72	(e) 81	(f) 63
5.	(a) 10	(b) 7	(c) 5
	(d) 6	(e) 8	(f) 9

War

Material: **Playing cards** with face cards removed**.**

Procedure: Shuffle the cards and deal them all out. Each player turns over one card from his pile. The player with the largest product gets all the cards. If two players have the same product, turn two more over to determine who gets the cards, or award the cards to the player whose two cards has the largest sum. The winner is the one with the most cards after all the cards are turned over.

Three in a row

Material: **Hundred-chart**, **counters** or coins for each player, **playing cards** with face cards removed.

Procedure: Shuffle cards and place them face down. Each player takes turns turning over a card and placing a counter on the chart covering a number that can be evenly divided by the number on the card. The first player with three counters in a row wins.

Variation: The first player whose counters form a path from one side of the board to the other wins.

Workbook Exercise 42

(2) Multiplication Algorithm with 9 (p. 88)

Multiply 2 and 3 digit numbers by 9.

Your student should be able to recall or quickly obtain the multiplication facts for 8. Continue with fact practice or games if necessary.

Learning Task 6, p. 83
Provide additional problems if necessary.

6. (a) 486 (b) 657 (c) 720
(d) 1809 (e) 6102 (f) 5481

Ask your student to mentally find the sum of the digits in each of the answers. If the sum is greater than 9, have him sum the digits of the answer again. The final answer will always be 9.
For example, for (f) 5 + 4 + 8 + 1 = 18; 1 + 8 = 9

War

Material: **Playing cards,** ace through 9 only, or 4 sets of number cards 1-9.

Procedure: Shuffle the cards and deal them all. Each player turns over three cards and forms one 2-digit number and one 1-digit number from them and multiplies them together. The player with the largest product gets all the cards that have been turned over for that round. The winner is the one with the most cards after all the cards are turned over.

Workbook Exercise 43

(3) Division Algorithm with 9 (p. 88)

Divide 2 and 3 digit numbers by 9.

Your student should know the division facts for 9. Continue with fact practice or games if necessary.

Learning Task 7, p. 88
Provide additional problems if necessary.

Before doing each division problem, ask your student to add the digits of the number being divided by 9, and then add the digits of the sum again until the final sum is a single digit. He should discover that if the final sum is 9, the answer will have no remainder. He may also discover that if the final sum is not 9, it is the same as the remainder. Since only (b) has no remainder, you may want to do additional problems to help him discover the pattern.

7.	(a) 10 r7	(b) 12	(c) 9 r8
	(d) 68 r8	(e) 100 r3	(f) 16 r1

War

Material: **Playing cards,** ace through 9 only, or 4 sets of number cards 1-9.

Procedure: Shuffle the cards and deal them all. Each player turns over three cards and forms one 2-digit number and one 1-digit number from them and divides the 2-digit number by the 1-digit number. The player with the smallest quotient gets all the cards that have been turned over for that round. The winner is the one with the most cards after all the cards are turned over.

Workbook Exercises 44-45

Unit 5 Money

Part 1 Dollars and Cents

(1) Dollars and Cents (pp. 91-92)

Read and write amounts of money in decimal notation and in words.
Count the amount of money in a set of bills and coins.
Convert dollars and cents to cents, and cents to dollars and cents.
Make change for $1.

This section is primarily a review of unit 3 in Primary Mathematics 2, but extends the amount of money to $100.

The concept of decimals has not yet been taught. The decimal point here should be considered to be a point separating dollars from cents. Decimals will be taught in *Primary Mathematics 4*.

➤ Ask your student how many cents are in a dollar. Remind him that when writing money, dollars are separated from cents with a dot. Remind him that he must always have two digits after the dot to indicate the number of cents. For example, ask him to write six dollars and five cents ($6.05), then six dollars and 50 cents ($6.50).

Page 91

➤ If your student needs practice counting money, provide this practice using either play or real money. Help him come up with strategies for counting coins if necessary. He can count first by quarters, then by 10's for dimes, then by 5's for nickels, and finally by 1's for pennies. He can also make 30 cents from a quarter and a nickel and then count dimes.

Write or say an amount less that $1.00 and have your student make change for $1.00 by counting out coins. For example, 42¢. The student hands you three pennies, saying "43, 44, 45" then a nickel, saying "50", then dimes or quarters, saying the amount of change as he hands the coins to you.

Ask your student for the number of
- nickels in a dollar
- dimes in a dollar
- quarters in a dollar
- dimes in four dollars
- quarters in six dollars
- nickels in three dollars
- etc.

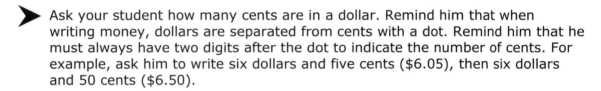

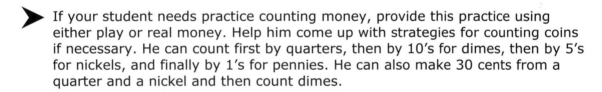

Learning Tasks 1-5, p. 92

You may want to have your student read the money amounts out loud. An "and" should be used for the dot. For example, in 1(a) he reads the amount as "seventy-four dollars and forty cents."

1. (a) **74** dollars **40** cents = $**74.40**
   (b) **7** dollars **61** cents = $**7.61**

2. (a) 125 (b) 1.70

3. (a) 30¢ (b) 195¢ (c) 405¢

4. (a) $0.85 (b) $1.60 (c) $3.45

5. (a) 0.30 (b) 0.45

Workbook Exercise 46

Part 2 Addition

(1) Addition of Money (pp. 94-96)

Add money within $100.

This section is primarily a review of unit 3 in Primary Mathematics 2, but extends the amount of money beyond $10 to $100.

Page 94

Use play or real money to illustrate the processes in the following learning tasks, if necessary. The student should trade in 100¢ for $1.

Learning Task 1-2, p. 95
The student can count up by tens and then fives or ones to add the cents, or use mental techniques involving making a 100:

Make a whole number of dollars. This method can be used when it is easy to mentally determine what number needs to be added to one set of money to make 100 with the sets, and to subtract that amount from the cents of the other set of money.
For example:

$46.25 + $0.85 = $47.10
/\
75¢ 10¢

Add a whole number of dollars, and then subtract the difference. This method can be used when the cents in one set of money is close to 100.
For example:

$34.85 + 95¢

95¢ is 5¢ less than $1. Add $1 to $34.85, and then subtract 5¢.

$34.85 + 95¢ = $34.85 + $1.00 – 5¢ = $35.85 – 5¢ = $35.80

Allow your student to choose the method he wishes to use with the learning tasks.

1. (a) $1.70 (b) $14.85 (c) $38.75
   (d) $3.00 (e) $26.00 (f) $34.00

2. (a) 3.05 (b) $3.30 (c) $6.10 (d) $17.40 (e) $25.65

Learning Task 3-4, p. 95
When adding amounts more than a dollar, we can add first the dollar amounts, and then the cents, using mental math techniques.

3. (a) 29.70; 29.80; 29.80 (b) 36.65; 37.00; 37.00
   (c) 35.80; 36.20; 36.20 (d) 34.70; 35.20; 35.20

4. (a) $20.85 (b) $38.00
   (c) $57.20 (d) $39.30
   (e) $60.50 (f) $55.10

Learning Task 5, p. 96
Money can be added using the same methods for adding whole numbers. The student can think of the money as a total number of cents. Have your student rewrite the problems, aligning the point separating dollars and cents.

5. (a) $56.70 (b) $38.00 (c) $74.30
   (d) $69.20 (e) $61.10 (f) $61.75

Workbook Exercise 47

(2) Word Problems (pp. 96-97)

Solve word problems involving the addition of money.

Encourage your student to draw models to solve the word problems, but do not insist on it if she can solve them easily without drawing models.

Learning Tasks 6-8, pp. 96-97

6. 9.75

7. 36.55

8. 9.10

Workbook Exercise 48

Part 3 Subtraction

(1) Subtraction of Money (pp. 98-100)

Subtract money within $100

This section is primarily review of unit 3 in Primary Mathematics 2, but extends the amount of money beyond $10 to $100.

Page 98

Use play or real money to illustrate the processes in the following learning tasks, if necessary.

Learning Task 1-3, p. 99

Your student can use mental techniques involving "making 100" to subtract cents.

<u>Subtract the cents from one of the dollars</u>.
For example:

$$\$36.25 - \$0.75 = ?$$

$36.25 → $35.25 and $1

$$\begin{aligned}\$36.25 - \$0.75 &= \$35.25 + \$0.25 \\ &= \$35.50\end{aligned}$$

<u>Subtract a whole number of dollars, and then add the difference</u>. This method can be easily used when the cents in the amount to be subtracted is close to 100, but some students may use it even with cent amounts smaller than 90¢. For example:

$64.25 - 95¢

95¢ is 5¢ less than $1. Subtract $1 from $64.25, and then add 5¢.

$64.25 - 95¢= $64.25 - $1.00 + 5¢ = $63.25 + 5¢ = $63.30

Allow your student to choose the method he wishes to use with the learning tasks.

1. (a) $2.40 (b) $8.45
   (c) $35.40 (d) $1.25
   (e) $6.05 (f) $46.45
2. (a) $0.40 (b) $0.70 (c) $0.90 (d) $0.55
3. (a) $2.40 (b) $13.75 (c) $45.80 (d) $31.20 (e) $41.75

Learning Tasks 4-5, p. 99

When adding amounts more than a dollar, the student can add first the dollar amounts, and then the cents, using mental math techniques.

4. (a) 12.80; 12.20; 12.20
   (b) 27.70; 27.50; 27.50

3d› *The number above the first arrow should be -$10.*
   (c) 17.20; 16.70; 16.70

5. (a) $35.50 (b) $34.85
   (c) $45.40 (d) $52.80
   (e) $9.70 (f) $27.25

Learning Task 6, p. 100

Money can be subtracted using the same algorithm for subtracting whole numbers. The student can think of the money as a total number of cents. Have your student rewrite the problems vertically, aligning the point separating dollars and cents.

6. (a) $21.70 (b) $25.50
   (c) $56.80 (d) $16.80
   (e) $41.45 (f) $29.90

➤ Review mental techniques for subtracting from one thousand. (See Enrichment 3 and Mental Math 9 in this manual).

For example, for 6200 – 415, the student can subtract 415 from 1000 by thinking of the number that needs to be added to 4 (the hundreds) to make 9, the number that needs to be added to 1 (the tens) to give 9, and the number that needs to be added to 5 (the ones) to give 10:

```
      6200 - 415 = 5200 + 585 = 5785
        /\
   5200 1000 - 415 = 585
```

In $62.00 – $4.15, the student can subtract 415¢ from 1000¢ to get 585¢, or $5.85, then add back in the $52.00. These problems can also be done by rewriting them vertically

---

Learning Task 7, p. 100

7. (a) 5785 (b) $57.85 (c) 3170 (d) $31.70

Review mental techniques for subtracting dollars and cents from ten dollars. Subtraction from \$10 can be done either as subtraction from 1000¢, as in the previous section, or by "counting up" as in making change.

For example, for \$30.00 – \$7.20, the student can "count up" to 10 and then 30:

$$\$7.20 \xrightarrow{+\ 80¢} \$8.00 \xrightarrow{+\ \$2} \$10.00 \xrightarrow{+\ \$20} \$30.00$$

$$\$30.00 - \$7.20 = \$22.80$$

These problems can also be done by rewriting them vertically.

Learning Task 8, p. 100

8. (a) \$5.30 (b) \$22.80 (c) \$41.75
   (d) \$26.20 (e) \$47.10 (f) \$60.55

Workbook Exercise 49

(2) Word Problems (pp. 100-101)

Solve word problems involving the subtraction of money.

Encourage your student to draw models to solve the word problems, but do not insist on it if she can solve them easily without drawing models.

Learning Tasks 9-11, pp. 100-101

9. \$4.35

10. \$5.40

11. \$9.50

Workbook Exercise 49 and 50
Workbook Reviews 5 and 6

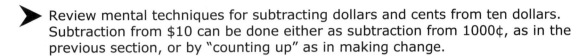

This page is blank

Answers to Workbook Exercises and Reviews

Exercise 1

1. (a) 1306 (b) 2048 (c) 1344 (d) 4066 (e) 8009
2. (a) 5278 (b) 2050 (c) 4207 (d) 6035
3. 2151, 4548, 3302, 1712, 3400, 6009, 4502
4. five thousand, four hundred seventeen
   six thousand, nine hundred forty
   eight thousand, fifty-three
   seven thousand, two hundred nine
   nine thousand, four

Exercise 2

1. (a) 8, 80, 400, 2000
   (b) 7, 40, 400, 6000 (c) 9, 90, 700, 7000
2. (a) 90 (b) 8 (c) 50 (d) 700
   (e) 3000 (f) 600 (g) 200
3. (a) 5, 8, 9, 7 (b) 5000 (c) 8, 800 (d) 9, 5
4. (a) 800 (b) 6 (c) 60 (d) tens (e) 5, 8

Exercise 3

1. (a) 4073 (b) 5001
2. (a) 4082 (b) 3671

US➤3. (a) less (b) less (c) greater
3d➤3. (a) smaller (b) smaller (c) greater

4. (a) 7640, 7604, 7406, 7064
   (b) 8709, 8790, 8907, 8970
5. (a) 932, 923, 392, 329, 239, 293
   (b) 872, 278
6. 8310
7. 2567

Exercise 4

1. (a) 6335 (b) 2316
2. (a) 395 (b) 590 (c) 4042 (d) 3507
   (e) 1183 (f) 2716 (g) 1225 (h) 4717
3. (a) 10 (b) 1000 (c) 1 (d) 100
   (e) 10 (f) 100 (g) 1000 (h) 1
4. (a) 1 (b) 100 (c) 1000 (d) 10
   (e) 1 (f) 1000 (g) 100 (h) 10
5. (a) 3809 (b) 5038 (c) 2987 (d) 1299
6. (a) 1302 (b) 903 (c) 4537 (d) 3698
7. 4044, 4054, 3734, 5635, 3634, 6634, 5633, 5632,
   3631, 5631, 6631, 2629, 2628, 2828, 2928

Exercise 5

1. (a) 16 (b) 2
2. +; 14
3. −; 7
4. 154
5. 430
6. 28
7. 125

Exercise 6

1. 150 − 16 = **134**
2. 15 + 4 = **19**
3. 42 − 29 = **13**
4. 21 − 12 = **9**
5. 42 kg − 39 kg = 3 kg
6. 10 + 36 = 46
7. 200 − 65 = 135
   She paid **$135** for the typewriter.

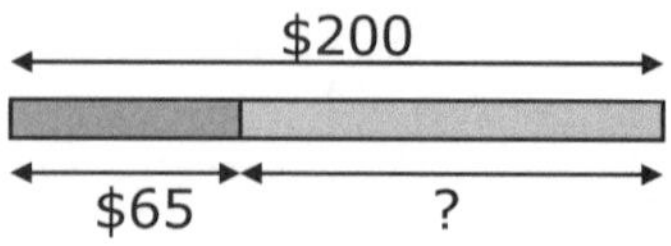

8. 145 + 28 = 173
He is **173 cm** tall.

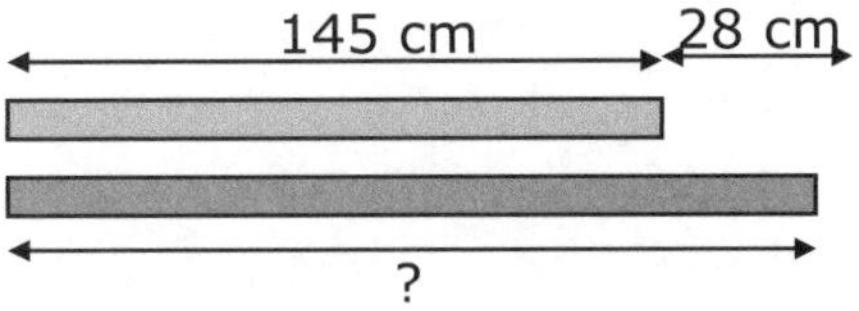

9. 45 + 379 = 424
He had **424** stamps.

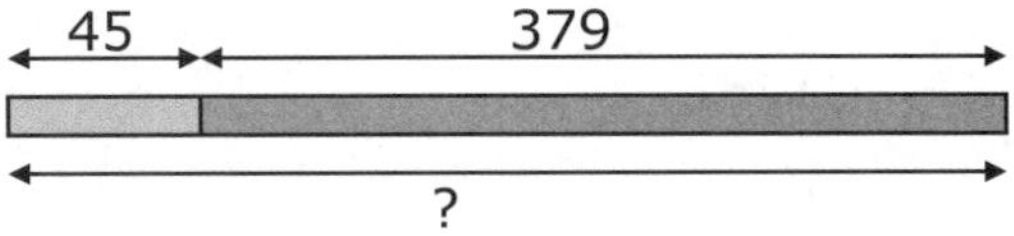

Exercise 7

1. (a) 135, 255
   (b) 120 + 15 = 135 There were **135** girls.
   (c) 120 + 135 = 255 There were **255** children altogether.
2. (a) 124, 12
   (b) 260 – 136 = 124 There are **124** girls
   (c) 136 – 124 = 12 There are **12** more boys than girls.
3. (a) Number of female workers = number of male workers – difference
   = 72 – 14
   = **58**
   (b) Total workers = number of male workers + number of female workers
   = 72 + 58
   = **130**
4. (a)

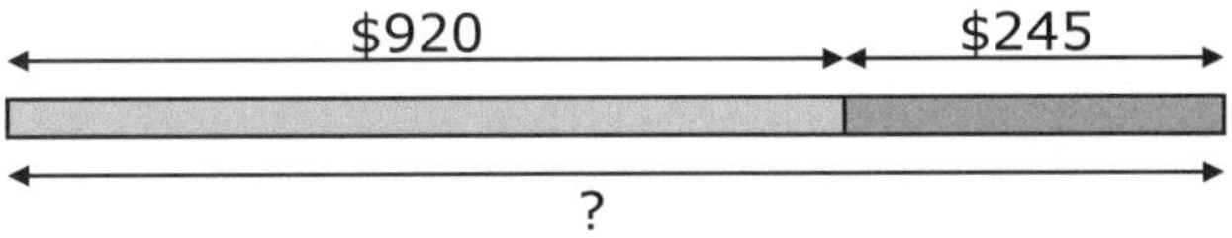

Total money = $920 + $245 = **$1165**
(b) (This diagram can also be used for (a).)

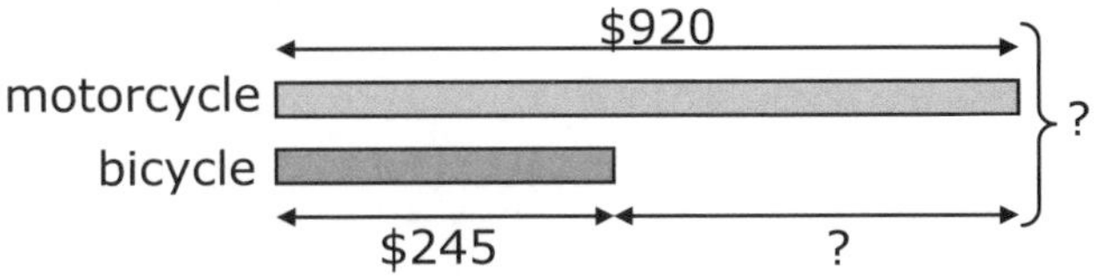

$920 – $245 = $675
The bicycle was **$675** cheaper than the motorcycle.

Exercise 8

1.

3627	5109	2780	5293
3674	5177	4965	4870
3824	5707	5954	6818
7624	8107	5591	7408
		9470	8934

2.
4112	7346	1818
6465	3074	8291
9937	5713	7179

VEGETABLES

3. 3872

4. 3546 + 632 = 4178
He collected **4178** stamps.

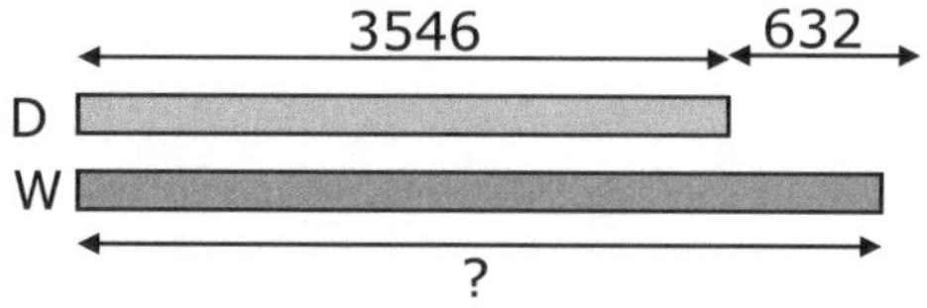

5. Total letters = letters delivered + letters left
= 1430 + 390
= **1820**

Exercise 8a (optional, in the appendix of this guide)

1
3521	9017	4342
4236	6412	8235
6671	8445	1555

2. 3862 + 594 = **4456**
3. 3480 + 676 = **4156**
4. (a) 7641 (b) 1467 (c) 7641 + 1467 = **9108**
5. 4368 + 3562 = 7930 Town C is **7930 miles** from Town A
6. (a) Number of girls = number of boys + difference = 2465 + 78 = **2543**
(b) Total = number of boys + number of girls = 2543 + 2465 = **5008**
7. No. 8 hundreds + 3 hundreds will require renaming to a thousand, so they will cost more than $2000.

Exercise 9

1.
A. 6661	B. 9192	C. 5215	
D. 3127	E. 7291	F. 9424	
G. 8692	H. 4154	I. 7260	tent

2. Total people = number on first night + number on 2nd night
= 2176 + 2745
= **4921**

3. Total money = money spent + money left
= $1138 + $862
= **$2000**

4. Cost of piano
= cost of computer + difference
= $1685 + $425
= **$2110**

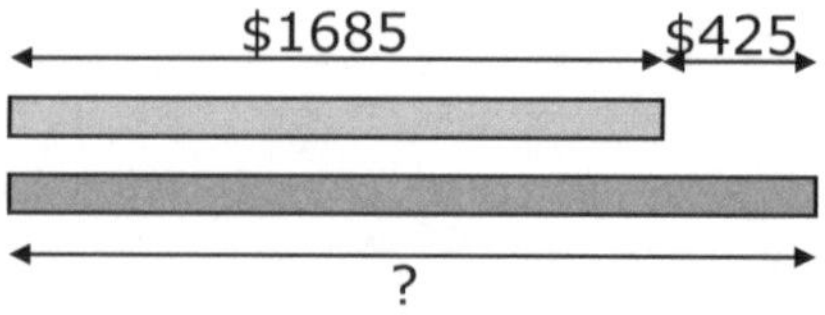

Exercise 10

1. 9322 6518 7400
   275 3313 8234
   5236 2593 1260 U

2. Number more adults = number of adults – number of children
   = 2546 – 1037
   = **1509**

3. Amount saved = total – amount spent
   = $1860 – $1248
   = **$612**

4. 3586 – 1864 = 1722
   She collected **1722**.

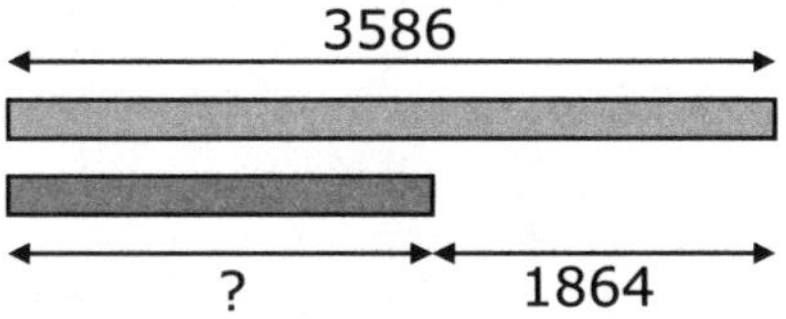

Exercise 11

1. 9388 9589 2329
   1516 3497 1129
   8194 8258 3729 COURTEOUS

2. 8272 2949 1872
   5785 6786 2837
   4726 3859 7683 **US>** PINEAPPLE
   3d>JACKFRUIT

Exercise 12

1.

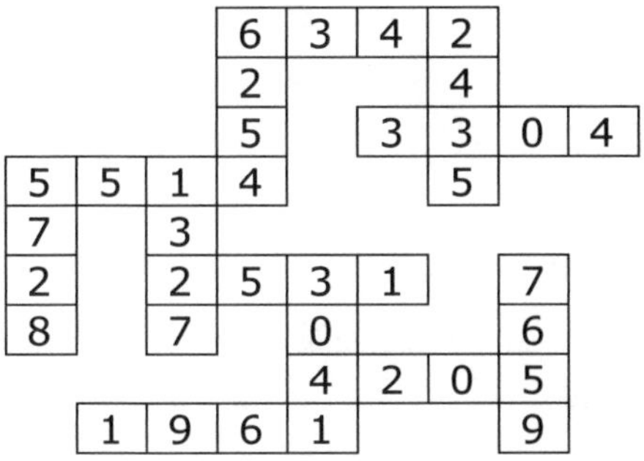

2. Number of books left = total books – number borrowed
   = 2040 – 1458
   = **582**

3. Number that were not birthday cards = total cards – birthday cards
= 3690 – 1861
= **1829**

4. Number of bricks he must get = total needed – number he already has
= 3606 – 2679
= **927**

Exercise 13

1. Total sticks = 1500 + 850
= 2350

Number eaten = 2350 - 264
= **2086**

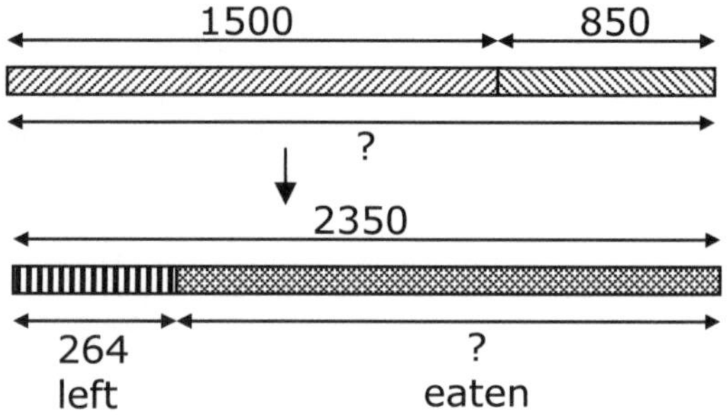

2. Amount he sold Sunday = 654 + 346 = 1000
Total number sold = 1000 + 654 = **1654**

3. Total adults = Number of men + number of women
= 1400 + 980
= 2380
Number of children = Total people – number of adults
= 3245 – 2380
= **865**

4. Amount Meilin saved = $1435 + $298
= $1733
Amount Alice saved = $1733 – $325
= **$1408**

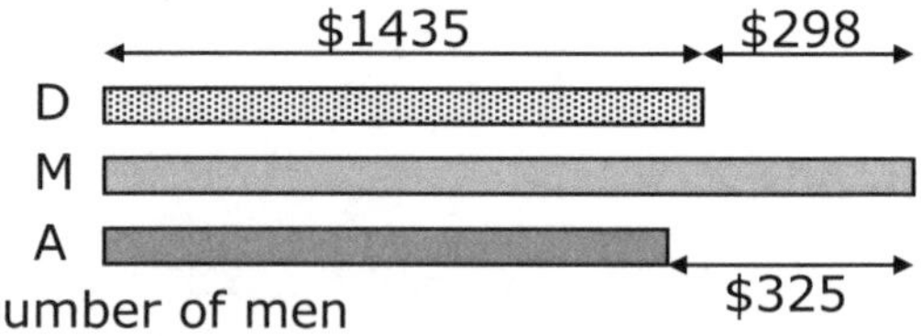

5. Number of women = total workers – number of men
= 2000 – 1340
= 660
Difference = number of men – number of women
= 1340 – 660
= **680**

6. Cost of refrigerator
= $2030 – $695
= $1335
Difference
= $1335 – $695
= **$640**

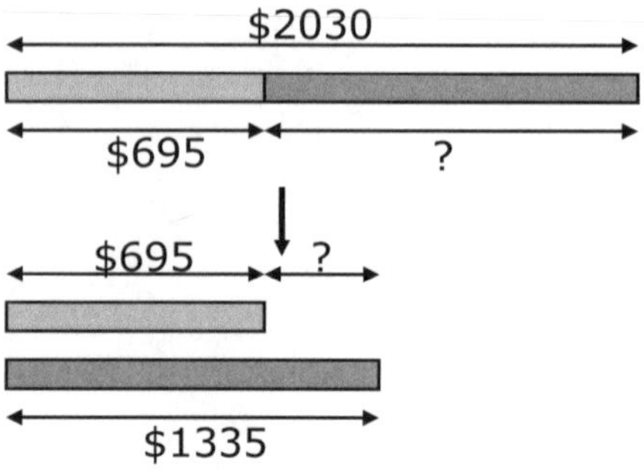

Review 1

1. (a) 271 (b) 5702 (c) 800 (d) 70

2. (a) greater (b) greater (c) greater
US➤ (d) less (e) less (f) greater
3d➤ (d) smaller (e) smaller (f) greater

3. (a) 20 (b) 4 (c) 3

4. (a) 340 (b) 318 (c) 5875
(d) 515 (e) 870 (f) 8061

5. 210, 450, 300

6. (a) 3034; 3234; 3234
(b) 1888; 1808; 1808
(c) 5452; 5460; 5460
(d) 2804; 2754; 2754

7. Total pages = pages read + pages left to read = 1445 + 258 = **1703**

8. Number of children = total - number of adults = 3521 - 2868 = **653**

9. Total needed = cost of motorcycle - amount he already has
= \$5430 - \$3350
= **\$2080**

10. Total spent = \$1430 + \$890
= \$2320
Money left = money she started with - total spent
= \$2790 - \$2320
= **\$470**

11. Number delivered Tuesday
= 1050 - 206
= 844
Total delivered
= 1050 + 844
= **1894**

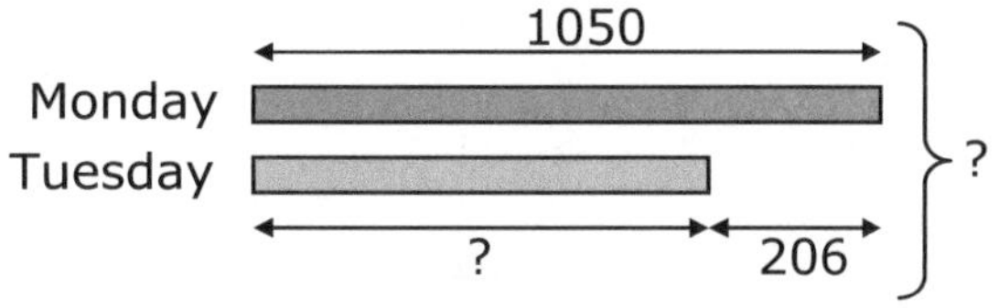

Exercise 14

1. (a) 24 (b) 15 (c) 8 (d) 15

2. (a) 9, 12, 15 (b) 12, 16, 20 (c) 15, 20, 25

3. (a) 8, 10, 12, 16 (b) 12, 15, 18, 24 (c) 16, 20, 28, 32, 36
(d) 20, 25, 35, 40 (e) 40, 50, 70, 80

Exercise 15

1. 27; 27
2. (a) 15; 15 (b) 28; 28
3. (a) 32; 32 (b) 12; 12 (c) 3; 27; 9; 27

Exercise 16

1. (a) 4; 4 (b) 3; 3
2. 5, 3
3.

6	9; 9	5; 5
7, 7	9, 9	5, 5
6, 6	9, 9	8, 8
2, 2	6, 6	9, 9

4. 4; 5; 4; 2; 3; 9; 9; 8; 7; 8; 9; 4; 8

Exercise 17

1.

	30	45	
0		100	36
	50	18	16
0	21	0	5
10	32		

2. 7; 10; 0; 6; 8; 9; 4; 5; 8; 3; 1; 0

Exercise 18

1. Total number of pears = number of bags x number of pears in each bag
   = 3 x 4
   = **12**
2. Number each child gets = total number ÷ number of children
   = 40 ÷ 5
   = **8**
3. Number of weeks = total money ÷ amount saved each week
   = 24 ÷ 4
   = **6**
4. Amount earned each day = total amount ÷ number of days
   = $45 ÷ 5
   = **$9**

5. Total length of cloth = length for each dress x number of dresses
   = 3 m x 8
   = **24 m**

6. Total liters of ice cream = number of tubs x amount in each tub
   = 6 x 2
   = **12 ℓ**

Exercise 19

1. Number of comic books = 7 x 3 = **21**
2. Amount saved in a week = $32 ÷ 4 = **$8**
3. Number of tigers = 20 ÷ 4 = **5**
4. (a) **15**, **20**
   (b) Cost of toy plane = 4 x $5 = **$20**
   (c) 3 x $5 = $15 or $20 – $5 = **$15**
5. (a) **32**, **8**
   (b) Amount saved = $24 ÷ 3 = **$8**
   (c) $8 x 4 = $32 or $24 + $8 = **$32**

Exercise 20

1. Total pages read = 8 x 4 = 32
   Total pages in book = 32 + 5 = **37**
2. Amount she spent = $47 – $20 = $27
   Cost of each kg = $27 ÷ 3 = **$9**
3. 1 unit = 8. She bought 1 unit more oranges. She bought 8 oranges.
   Or: Total oranges bought = 2 x 18 = 16.
   Amount more oranges bought = 16 – 8 = **8**

4. Length of pole = 1 unit
   Length of rope = 8 units
   Length of one piece = 8 units ÷ 2
   = 2 units
   2 units = 2 x 3 m = 6 m
   Or:
   Length of rope = 8 x 3 m = 24 m
   Length of one piece = 24 m ÷ 4 = **6 m**

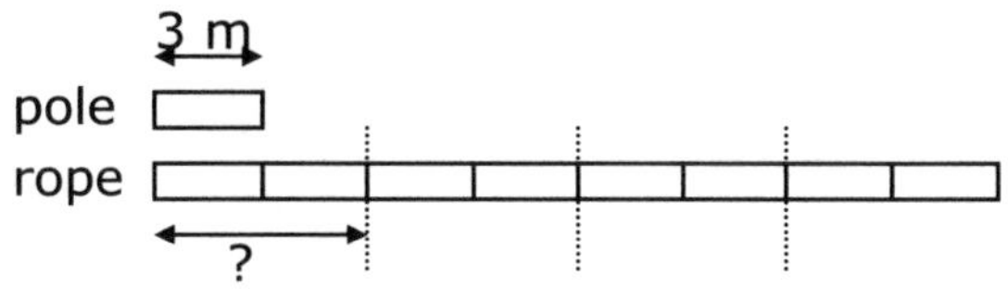

Exercise 21

1.	12, 120	21, 210	
	15, 150	20, 200	
	18, 1800	24, 2400	
	28, 2800	24, 2400	**3d➤** *The 2001printing shows the last problem as 600 x 5. It should be 600 x* ***4*** *= 2400*

2.		180	400
	1500	1000	2400
	3000	240	2700
	1200	140	3600

Exercise 22

1.	A. 48	R. 84	E. 68
	S. 128	R. 255	
	T. 368	U. 168	E. 288

TREASURE Island

2. (a) 205 (b) 156

3. (a) 129 (b) 248 (c) 355

Exercise 23

1.	74	135	116	344
	185	115	96	228
	195	86	316	490

2. 104, 54, 183, 72, 140, 144, 135, 136, 130, 177, 200, 280, 400, 388, 224

3. Total passengers = 46 x 3 = **138**

4 Total ribbon = 75 cm x 5 = **375 cm**

5. Total savings = $60 x 4 = **$240**

Exercise 24

1.	A. 248	R. 484	E. 1065	
	W. 1000	E. 906	T. 748	
	V. 912	A. 546	S. 868	SAVE WATER

2.	435	1540
	1056	990
	4000	1400
	326	2100
	1070	3348
	540	1107

3. Total payment = 240 x $3 = **$720**
4. Total = 104 x 4 = **416**
5. Cost of motorcycle
   = $385 x 5 = **$1925**

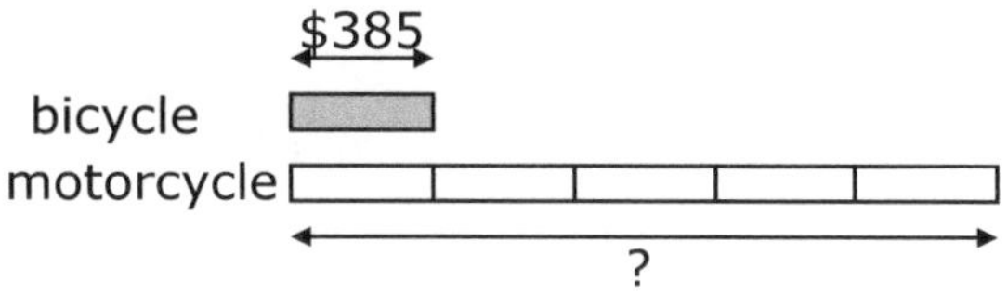

Exercise 25

1. M. 7 r1 T. 20 E. 31 r1
   U. 14 r1 K. 15 O. 43
   N. 48 R. 41 r1 Y. 49 r1
   MONKEY TURKEY

2 goose

Review 2

1. (a) 942 (b) 4605 (c) 3004 (d) 6030
2. (a) four thousand, sixty-two
   (b) five thousand, eight hundred eighty
3. 2040, 2030, 2130, 2136, 2186, 1186
4. (a) 2000 (b) 1108 (c) 3445 (d) 8674
5. (a) 980 (b) 1010 (c) 978 (d) 2109
6. (a) 309 (b) 2090 (c) 9009 (d) 4779
7. Number of brown beads = 1407 + 795 = **2202**
8. Amount saved = $1000 - $832 = **$168**
9. Total eggs used = 18 x 4 = **72**
10. Number of women = 650 x 2 = 1300
    Total workers = 650 + 1300 = **1950**
11. Total number of chickens and ducks left = 650 + 520 = 1170
    Total sold = 2000 - 1170 = **830**

Review 3

1.

x	1	2	3	4	5	6	7	8	9	10
2	2	4	6	8	10	12	14	16	18	20
3	3	6	9	12	15	18	21	24	27	30
4	4	8	12	16	20	24	28	32	36	40
5	5	10	15	20	25	30	35	40	45	50
10	10	20	30	40	50	60	70	80	90	100

Number of bags	2	3	5	7	9	10
Total Weight	20 kg	30 kg	50 kg	70 kg	90 kg	100 kg

2. 5 x 3 = 15; 3 x 5 = 15; 15 ÷ 3 = 5; 15 ÷ 5 = 3
3. (a) 1, 50, 700, 3000 (b) 3, 70, 0, 7000
4. (a) 15 (b) 9000 (c) 5
   (d) tens (e) 10 (f) 106 , 2
5. (a) 12 (b) 32 (c) 40 (d) 8
6. Stickers still needed = 400 – 199 = **201**
7. Glasses from one bottle = 96 ÷ 4 = **24**

3d➤8. Cost of typewriter = $175 x 3 = **$525**
US➤8. Cost of computer = $175 x 3 = **$525**

9. 1200 – 860 = 340
   860 – 340 = 520
   He had **520** more.

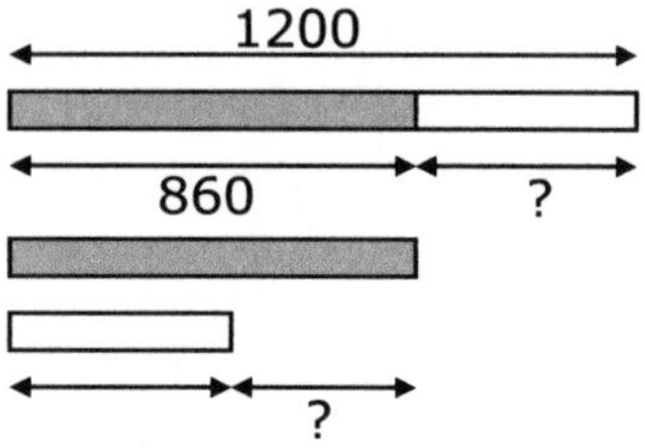

10. Cost of television = $1900 – $650
    = $1250
    Cost of both = $1900 + $1250
    = **$3150**

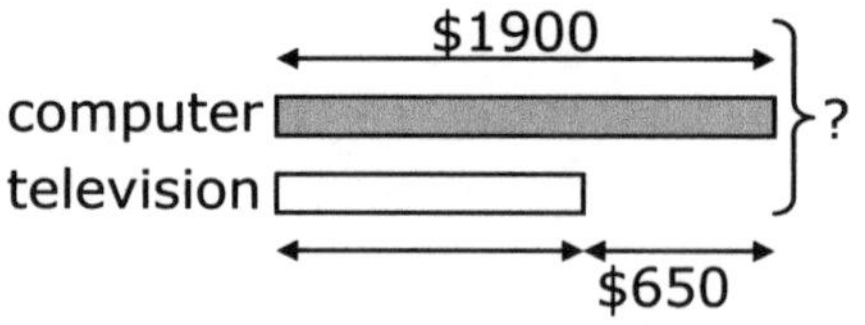

Exercise 26

1. 41 r1 16 r1
   13 r2 32 r0
   37 r1 19 r2
   26 r2 19 r0
2. 74 ÷ 3 = 24 r2 There were **24** in each jar with **2** left over.
3. Total bunches sold = 70 ÷ 5 = **14**
4. Number of groups = 96 ÷ 4 = **24**

Exercise 27

1. C. 86 E. 86 r1 M. 82
   O. 128 P. 201 R. 314
   S. 204 T. 250 U. 82 r3
   COMPUTERS
2. Amount saved a month = $900 ÷ 4 = **$225**
3. 186 ÷ 5 = 37 r1 There were **37** students. **1** sticker was left over.
4. Tickets sold by each student = 243 ÷ 3 = **81**

Exercise 28

1. (a) 6, 12, 16
   (b) 18, 24, 30
   (c) 20, 36, 40
   (d) 25, 40, 50, 55
   (e) 50, 60, 90
2. (a) 6, 9, 15, 18, 21, 24, 30
   (b) 8, 12, 16, 24, 28, 36, 40
   (c) 10, 15, 25, 30, 35, 40, 45, 50
   (d)

x	1	2	3	4	5	6	7	8	9	10
3	3	6	9	12	15	18	21	24	27	30
4	4	8	12	16	20	24	28	32	36	40
5	5	10	15	20	25	30	35	40	45	50
10	10	20	30	40	50	60	70	80	90	100

3. (a) 10 (b) 16
   (c) 27 (d) 18
   (e) 60 (f) 16
   (g) 35 (h) 10
   (i) 32 (j) 35
4. 6, 6 10, 10
   8, 8 9, 9
   6, 6 7, 7
   4, 4 9, 9
5. (a) 9 (b) 9
   (c) 3 (d) 8
   (e) 7 (f) 5
   (g) 6 (h) 4
   (i) 6 (j) 3

Exercise 29

1. (a) 30, 30 (b) 36, 36
   (c) 42, 42 (d) 48, 48
   (e) 54, 54 (f) 60, 60
2. 6, 18, 30, 48, 36, 12, 24, 54, 60, 42

Exercise 30

1. (1) 2 (2) 3 (3) 10 (4) 8
   (5) 5 (6) 9 (7) 7 RAINBOW

2. | | |
   |---|---|
   | 6 | 2 |
   | 30 | 7 |
   | 18 | 1 |
   | 42 | 4 |
   | 36 | 10 |
   | 54 | 9 |
   | 60 | 5 |
   | 24 | 3 |
   | 12 | 0 |

Exercise 31

1.

	2	2	8	
	7			
3	0		5	
1		1	4	4
2	1	0		0
		2	8	8

2. | | | |
   |---|---|---|
   | 258 | 450 | 588 |
   | 1836 | 2700 | 3444 |
   | 4746 | 4800 | 5538 |

Exercise 32

1. T. 8 r5 N. 12 r3 G. 14
   P. 10 r4 A. 8 r1
   O. 16 E. 6 r2 N. 9 r5
   PENTAGON

2. | | | |
   |---|---|---|
   | 15 r2 | 14 r0 | 13 r0 |
   | 133 r2 | 100 r5 | 91 r0 |
   | 82 r4 | 119 r5 | 153 r5 |

Exercise 33

1. Money received = \$45 x 6 = **\$270**
2. Number of times it beats in 6 minutes = 72 x 6 = **432**

3. 153 ÷ 6 = 25 r3 Number of bags = **25**, number of tomatoes left over = **3**
4. Number of bunches = 462 ÷ 6 = 77
   Money received = 77 x $5 = **$385**
5. Number of pieces = 408 ÷ 6 = 68
   Number of pieces left = 68 - 32 = **36**
6. Number of coffee bags used in 4 weeks = 20 x 6 = 120
   Number of coffee bags used in 1 week = 120 ÷ 4 = **30**
7. Total stamps = 208 + 186 = 394
   394 ÷ 6 = 65 r4 There were **65** packets and **4** stamps left over.

Exercise 34

1. 21 42 28
   56 35
   49 63
   70 14 7
2. (a) 4 (b) 6 (c) 5 (d) 7 (e) 9
   (f) 1 (g) 10 (h) 2 (i) 3 (j) 8
3. (1) 14 (2) 7 (3) 28 (4) 10
   (5) 56 (6) 3 (7) 49 (8) 5
   FLAMINGO

Exercise 35

1. 560 378 273
   497 434 301
   686 245 532
2. 672 315 574
   4900 2296 1015
   2821 4578 3717
   PRAYING MANTIS

Exercise 36

1. $7\overline{)80} \rightarrow 11$ r3 $7\overline{)55} \rightarrow 7$ r6 $7\overline{)69} \rightarrow 9$ r6 $7\overline{)43} \rightarrow 6$ r1
   $7\overline{)98} \rightarrow 14$ $7\overline{)76} \rightarrow 10$ r6 $7\overline{)84} \rightarrow 12$
2. E. 13 U. 19 r2 N. 65 G. 133 r1
   P. 110 I. 114 r5 N. 88 r3 S. 102 r2
   PENGUINS

Exercise 37

1. Total meters jogged = 400 x 7 = **2800 m**
2. Total number of buckets the tank holds = 637 ÷ 7 = **91**
3. Number of kilograms = $98 ÷ $7 = **14 kg**
4. Total number of books = $301 ÷ $7 = 43
   Number of books he carried = 43 − 18 = **25**
5. Number of grams in each bag = 875 ÷ 7 = 125
   Number of grams in the box = 125 x 6 = **625**

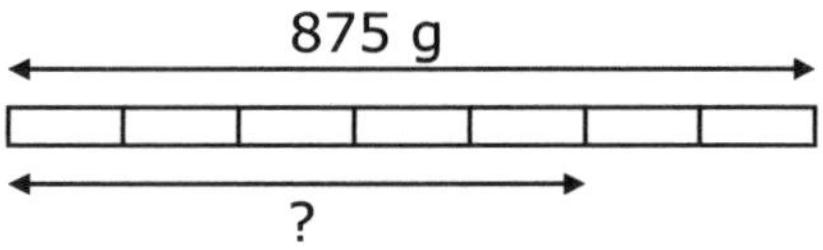

6. Length of 7 planks = 7 x 3 m = 21 m
   Total length = 21 + 2 = **23 m**
7. Total number of boys = 5 x 7 = 35
   Total girls = 84 − 35 = **49**
   or: Number of children in each group = 84 ÷ 7 = 12
   Girls in each group = 12 − 5 = 7
   Total girls = 7 x 7 = 49

Review 4

1. (a) 5306 (b) 8005 (c) 10,000
2. (a) 4320 (b) 8320 (c) 2645

US➤3. (a) less (b) less (c) less
3d➤3. (a) smaller (b) smaller (c) smaller

4. (a) 800 (b) 80 (c) 8
5. (a) 1150 (b) 1000 (c) 3661
   (d) 102 r6 (e) 200 (f) 1400
6. (a) 420 + 180 = **600**
   (b) 300 + 100 = **400**
   (c) 600 − 400 = **200**
7. Total students taking lessons = 125 + 11 = **136**
8. Difference = $35 − $12 = **$23**
9. Number of guppies = 15 x 3 = **45**
10. Money saved in 1 month = $3000 − $2200 = $800
    Money saved in 6 months = $800 x 6 = **$4800**
11. Number of packets = 600 ÷ 6 = 100
    Number of packets left = 100 − 45 = **55**

Exercise 38

1. 32 56 24
   40 64 48
   72 16 80
2. 3, 5, 8, 2, 6, 4, 9, 7, 10

Exercise 39

1. (1) 256 (2) 432 (3) 400 (4) 504 (5) 704
   (6) 216 (7) 288 (8) 112 (9) 736
   EXCELLENT
2.

3	6	8		5		4	6	4
	4			1	9	9	2	
	2		4	9	6		7	
4	4	0		2	0	3	2	

Exercise 40

1. 7 r2 8 r3 6 r1
   11 9 r5 12
   4 r4 9 5r3
   frog
2. F. 106 r2 O. 120 r2 P. 46 r4
   K. 75 r2 R. 66 T. 94 r2
   X. 12 r7 S. 61 C. 93 r4
   EXERCISE TO KEEP FIT

Exercise 41

1. Amount used in 8 months = 185 x 8 = **1480 ℓ**
2. Kilograms sold = \$96 ÷ \$8 = **12**
3. 900 ÷ 8 = 112 r4 There were **112** in each box, with **4** left over.
4. Number of red roses
   = 145 x 8 = 1160
   Number more red roses
   = 1160 – 145 = **1015**
   or: Number more red roses
   = 145 x 7 = 1015

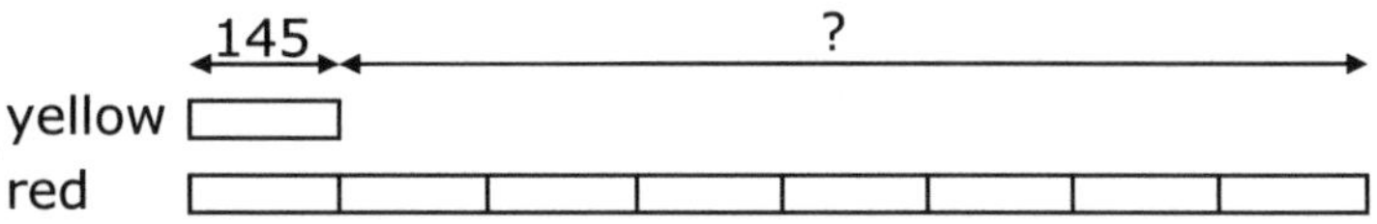

5. Amount of tickets each student sold = 272 ÷ 8 = 34
   Money collected by each student = 34 x $3 = **$102**
   Or: Total money = 272 x $3 = $816
   Money collected by each student = $816 ÷ 8 = $102

6. Total donuts = 4 x 6 = 24
   Number each person received = 24 ÷ 8 = **3**

7. Apples in boxes = 8 x 10 = 80
   Total apples = 80 + 4 = **84**

Exercise 42

1. 27 45
   90 36
   18 63 54
   81 72

2. (down) 9, 3, 8, 5
   10, 4, 7, 6

Exercise 43

1. 126 189 720
   891 792 477
   360 567 648

2. M. 675 L. 954 E. 2376
   I. 4131 N. 4707 A. 5508
   P. 7056 C. 7470 O. 8523
   POLICEMAN

Exercise 44

1. 27 ÷ 9 = 3 80 ÷ 9 = 8 r8 11 = 99 ÷ 9;
   90 ÷ 9 = 10 6 r5 = 59 ÷ 9 25 ÷ 9 = 2 r7

2. 103 r2; 61 r5; 73; 42 r3; 23; 48 r4; 94 r6

Exercise 45

1. Total cost = $9 x 56 = **$504**

2. Number of groups = 108 ÷ 9 = **12**

US➤3. Total pounds sold = $342 ÷ $9 = **38 lb**
3d➤3. Total kilograms sold = $342 ÷ $9 = **38 kg**

4. Total number of children = 249 + 255 = 504
   Number of children in each row = 504 ÷ 9 = **56**

5. Number of pieces = 414 ÷ 9 = 46
   Each of the 46 pieces is cut into 4 parts.
   Number of parts = 46 x 4 = **184**

6. Total number of plates = 9 x 10 = 90
   Number left = 90 - 25 = **65**

7. Total number of people sharing the cost = 4 + 5 = 9
   Amount each paid = $117 ÷ 9 = **$13**

Exercise 46

1. (a) 30.85 (b) 4.30 (c) 80.07

2. (a) $5.65 (b) $10.08 (c) $17.70
   (d) $90.12 (e) $320.04 (f) $1030.00

3. (a) eighty cents
   (b) one dollar and thirty-six cents
   (c) six dollars and forty-four cents
   (d) seven dollars and ninety-eight cents
   (e) twenty-three dollars and twenty cents
   (f) ten dollars and five cents
   (g) forty-four dollars and fifty-five cents
   (h) four hundred twelve dollars
   (i) three thousand, seven hundred nine dollars

Exercise 47

1. (a) 11.90, 11.95 (b) 9.85, 10.25
   (c) 34.35, 35.10 (d) 66.35, 67.20

2. (a) $31.30 (b) $35.10
   (c) $69.15 (d) $53.40

3. (a) 1000; $10.00
   (b) 3115; $31.15
   (c) 9485; $94.85
   (d) 10,000; $100.00

4. A. $4.95 E. $16.35 G. $17.60
   I. $80.29 L. $93.73 N. $85.20
   R. $43.85 S. $53.14 T. $73.90
   TRIANGLES

Exercise 48

1. (a) 11.90 (b) 5.90 (c) 20.55
   (d) 13.85 (e) 4.90 (f) 41.40
2. Total money = $92.65 + $79.80 = **$172.45**
3. Total cost = $62.05 + $98.83 = **$160.88**
4. Cost of television set
   = $80.80 + $98.70
   = **$179.50**

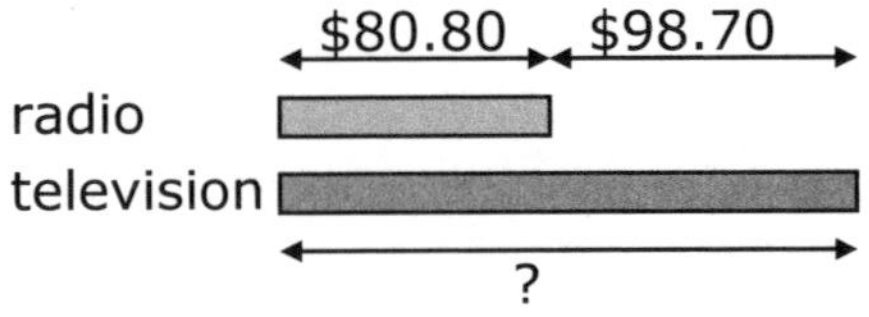

Exercise 49

1. (a) 2.50, 2.45 (b) 2.35, 1.55
   (c) 12.00, 11.40 (d) 17.05, 16.60
2. (a) $5.15 (b) $4.05
   (c) $53.60 (d) $53.55
3. (a) 5250; $52.50
   (b) 2525; $25.25
   (c) 4520; $45.20
   (d) 3515; $35.15
4. $37.20 $25.50 $16.15
   $63.45 $16.55 $7.01
   $35.95 $15.85 $9.90
   BADMINTON

Exercise 50

1. (a) $2.25 (b) $1.35 (c) $1.00 (d) $25.45 (e) $2.10
2. Cost of watch = $60.25 − $16.90 = **$43.35**
3. Amount she spent
   = $48.60 − $3.55
   = **$45.05**

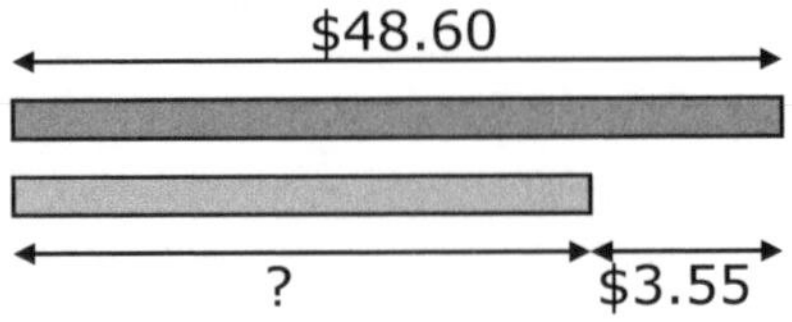

4. Difference = $70 − $47.95 = **$22.05**

Exercise 51

1. Total spent = \$24.95 + \$9.50 = \$34.45
   Change = \$50 – \$34.45 = **\$15.55**

2. Cost of bat = \$1.20 + \$2.60 = \$3.80
   Total spent = \$3.80 + \$1.20 = **\$5.00**

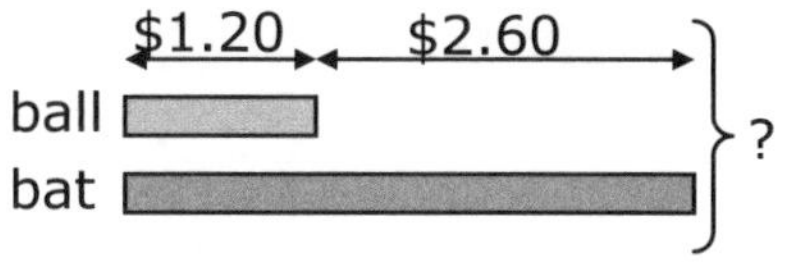

3. Amount spent
   = \$10.00 – \$2.05 = \$7.95
   Cost of pen
   = \$7.95 – \$7.35 = **\$0.60**

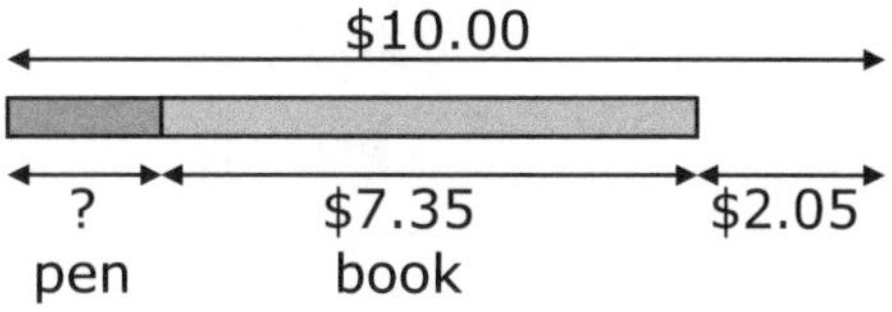

4. Cost of lunch
   = \$3.80 – \$1.15 = \$2.65
   Total money
   = \$3.80 + \$2.65 = **\$6.45**

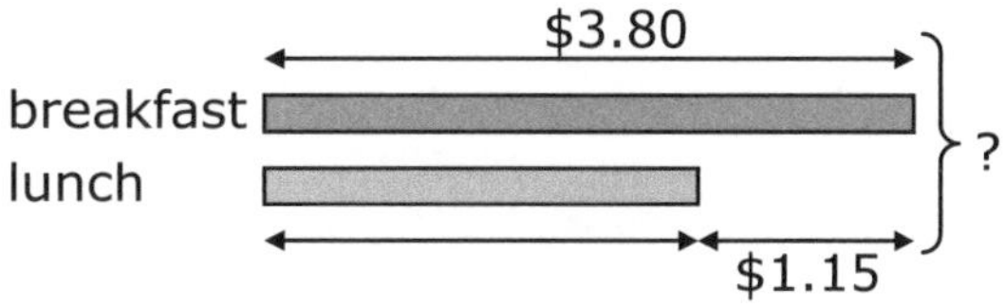

Review 5

1. (a) \$200 (b) B
2. (a) five thousand, seven
   (b) one thousand, forty-three
   (c) nine thousand, five hundred sixty
3. 5000
4. 800
5. 4
6. 2; 200
7. 3263; 2030
8. (a) 6553 (b) 3944 (c) 9107 (d) 4590
9. | 450 | | 18 | |
   | 9 |
   | 288 | | 36 | |

10. Number more that visited Sunday = 3300 – 2950 = **350**
11. Total rice = 905 kg + 145 kg = **1050 kg**
12. Total number of oranges = 50 x 7 = **350**

13. Number of non-rotten oranges = 928 – 16 = 912
    Number of bags = 912 ÷ 9 = **114**

14. Total spent = \$500 + \$1250 = \$1750
    Amount saved = \$2500 – \$1750 = **\$750**

Review 6

1. (a) 4070 (b) 1400 (c) 6019 (d) 4900
2. (a) 900 (b) 598 (c) 671
3. (a) 2638 (b) 2754 (c) 6156 (d) 48 r8
4. (a) Larger number = 24 + 50 = **74**

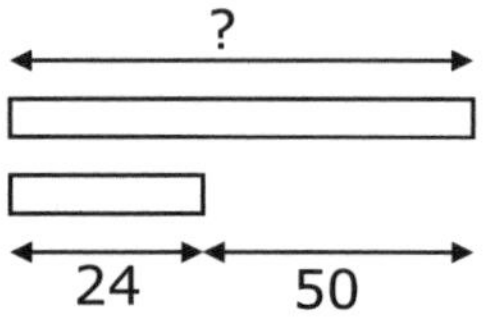

   (b) 9 x ? = 72
   ? = 72 ÷ 9 = **8**

5. Amount each child paid = \$42 ÷ 6 = **\$7**
6. Weight last year = 52 kg – 8 kg = **44 kg**
7. Total number of sticks = 1325 + 576 = **1901**

US➤8. Weight of pineapples = 150 lb + 112 lb = **262 lb**
3d➤8. Weight of durians = 150 kg + 112 kg = **262 kg**

9. 108 ÷ 5 = 21 r3 There were **21** bags with **3** apples left over.
10. Weight of 8 notebooks = 800 g – 200 g = 600 g
    Weight of 1 notebook = 600 g ÷ 8 = **75 g**
11. Cost of crabs = 9 x \$12 = \$108
    Total money = \$108 + \$110 = **\$218**

Answers to Textbook Practices and Reviews

Practice 1A (p. 12)

1. (a) 2163 (b) 8008 (c) 3600 (d) 1376 (e) 4005
2. (a) one thousand, three hundred forty-seven
   (b) five thousand, nine hundred
   (c) seven thousand, fifty eight
3. (a) 6000 + 300 + 50 + 2
   (b) 4000 + 90 + 1
   (c) 7000 + 4
4. (a) 1205 (b) 3020 (c) 2032
5. (a) 1736 (b) 7504 (c) 90
   (d) 800 (e) 3 (f) 900
6. (a) 3776 (b) 2060

Practice 1B (p. 13)

US➤1. (a) less (b) greater (c) greater
(d) less (e) less (f) less

3d➤1. (a) smaller (b) greater (c) greater
(d) smaller (e) smaller (f) smaller

2. (a) 7711 (b) 8812
3. (a) 9099 (b) 8445
4. 1260, 1098, 989, 208
5. 350, 3005, 3050, 3500, 5003

Practice 1C (p. 17)

1. (a) 800 (b) 8 (c) 8000 (d) 80
2. 5 stands for 5000
   6 stands for 600
   2 stands for 20
   9 stands for 9
3. (a) 4; 40 (b) 0; 0
4. (a) 2010, 2011, 2012
   (b) 5642, 5652, 5662
   (c) 2100, 2200, 2300
   (d) 7056, 8056, 9056

5. (a) 1000 (b) 2009 (c) 5780 (d) 5000 (e) 4040
6. (a) 5399 (b) 3520 (c) 2350 (d) 5160 (e) 5692

Practice 2A (p. 22)

1. (a) 874 (b) 408 (c) 802
2. (a) 1000 (b) 400 (c) 800
3. (a) 480 (b) 564 (c) 155
4. (a) 248 (b) 438 (c) 150
5. Total rubber bands = amount she had + amount friend gave her
   = 254 + 58
   = **312**
6. Number eaten = total – amount left
   = 650 – 39
   = **611**
7. Other number = sum – one number
   = 175 – 49
   = **126**
8. Bigger number = smaller number + difference
   = 153 + 68
   = **221**
9. smaller number = bigger number – difference
   = 126 – 48
   = **78**

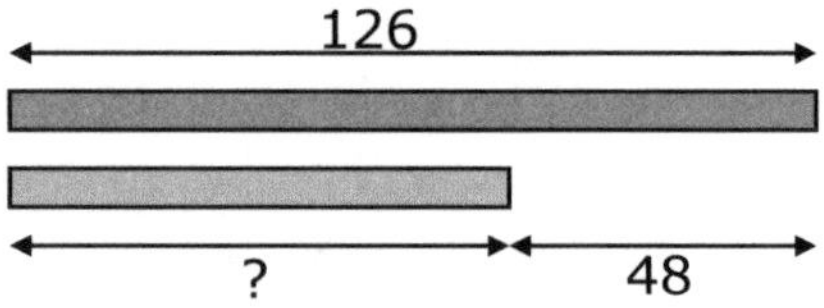

Practice 2B (p. 23)

1. (a) 1043 (b) 484 (c) 426
2. (a) 908 (b) 494 (c) 1143
3. (a) 430 (b) 123 (c) 218
4. (a) 99 (b) 329 (c) 13
5. Total money = cost of television set + amount left
   = \$850 + \$450
   = **\$1300**

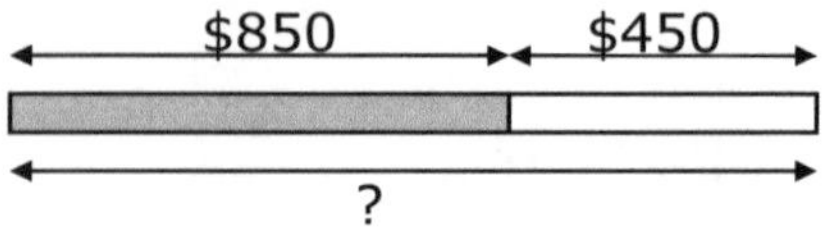

6. Tickets sold Saturday = tickets sold Sunday – difference
   = 429 – 64
   = **365**

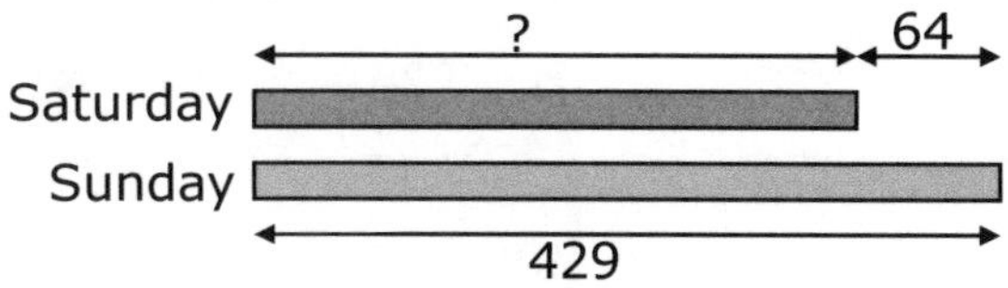

7. (a) Total for A and B = 468 + 652 = **1120**
   (b) Total for A, B, and C = 1120 + 945 = **2065**

8. (a) Total sold = Tickets sold yesterday + tickets sold today
   = 35 + 15
   = **24**

   (b) Tickets not sold = total – tickets sold
   = 35 – 24
   = **11**

9.

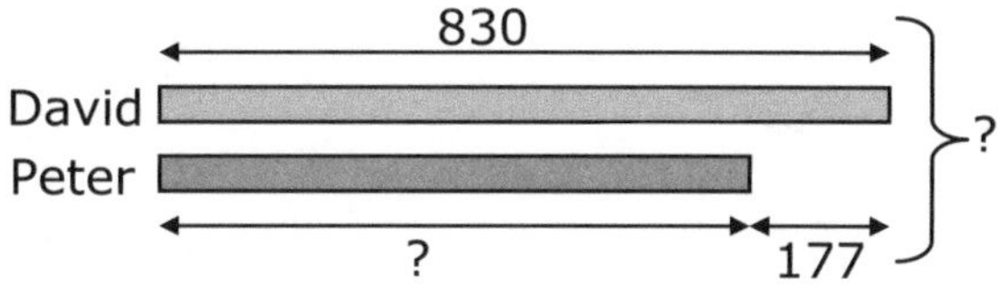

   (a) Amount Peter collected = 830 – 177 = **653**

   (b) Total collected = 880 + 653 = **1483**

Practice 2C (p. 34)

1. (a) 9779 (b) 4895 (c) 4251
2. (a) 8960 (b) 8000 (c) 3414
3. (a) 7564 (b) 869 (c) 2564
4. (a) 5334 (b) 4595 (c) 879
5. Total sold = 957 + 1238 = **2195**
6. Difference = 2545 – 1730 = **815**
7. Money he donated = $1450 – $935 = **$1487**
8. Difference = $3265 – $2955 = **$310**
9. Number that went by ferry = 1147 + 3996 = **5143**
10. Amount her brother saved = $2900 + $1567 = **$4467**

Practice 2D (p. 35)

1. (a) 7180 (b) 6520 (c) 4049
2. (a) 9887 (b) 6903 (c) 4256
3. (a) 9042 (b) 1872 (c) 1687
4. (a) 7703 (b) 2429 (c) 3519
5. Number of children = 2055 – 1637 = **418**
6. Number present = 1206 – 47 = **1159**
7. Number of tickets = 2316 – 1548 = **768**
8. Difference = \$2005 – \$1542 = **\$463**
9. (a) Total spent = \$2572 + \$955 = **\$3527**
   (b) Amount left = \$5000 – \$3527 = **\$1473**
10. (a) Number fewer = 1225 – 904 = **321**
    (b) Total students = 1225 + 904 = **2129**

Practice 2E (p. 38)

1. Number of duck eggs = 1930 – 859
   = 1071
   Total eggs = 1930 + 1071
   = **3001**

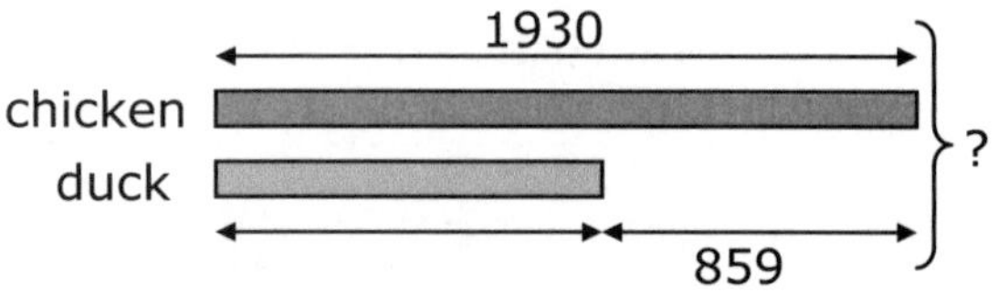

2. Number of girls = 4100 – 2680
   = 1420
   Number more boys = 2680 – 1420
   = **1260**

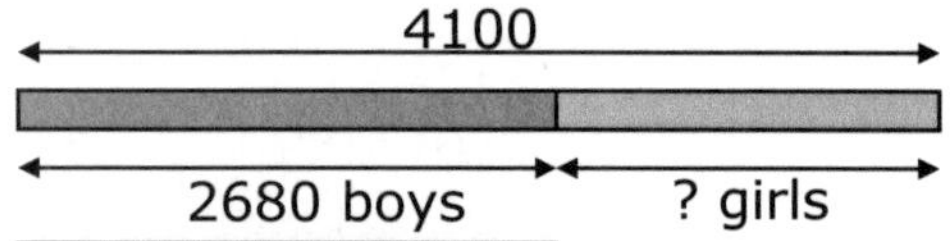

3. Total = 1050 + 950 = 2000
   Number left = 2000 – 1765 = **235**

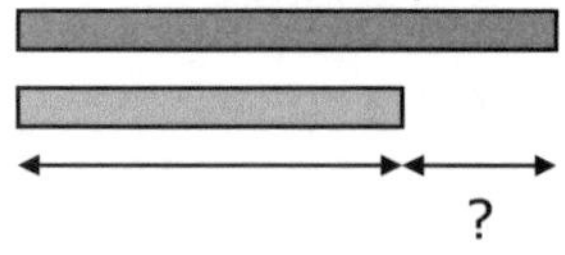

4. Total spent = \$1268 + \$1380 = \$2648
   Amount left = \$3915 – \$2648 = **\$1267**

5. Cost of oven = \$1739 – \$850
   = \$889
   Total cost = \$1739 + \$850
   = **\$2628**

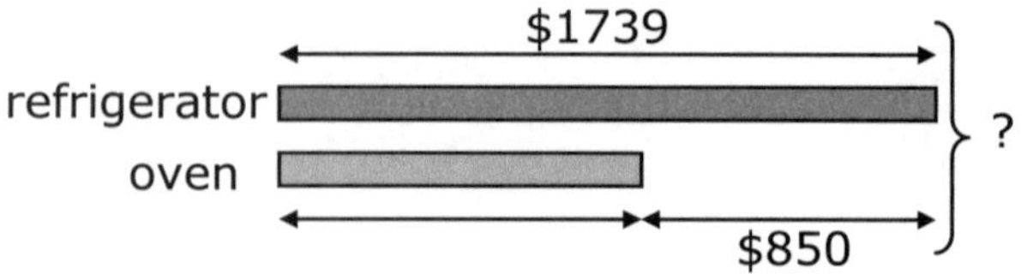

6. Money in bank
   = \$2467 + \$133
   = \$2600
   More money needed
   = \$3000 – \$2600
   = **\$400**

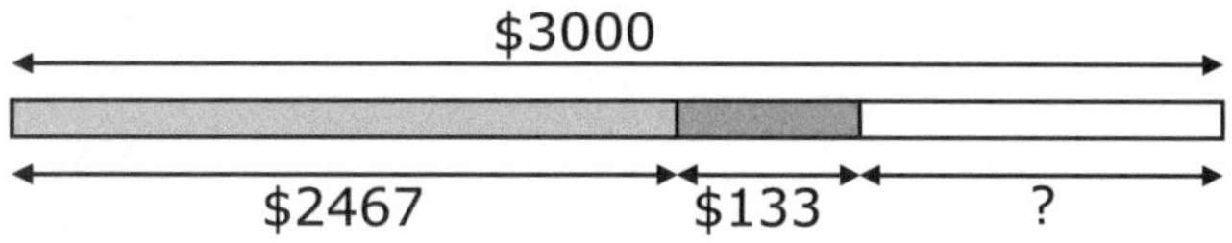

7. Total adults = total men + total women = 2745 + 855 = 3600
   Number of children = total people – total adults = 4608 – 3600 = **1008**

8. Amount Miss Wang saved
   = \$1035 + \$278
   = \$1313
   Amount Miss Wu saved
   = \$1313 – \$105
   = \$1208

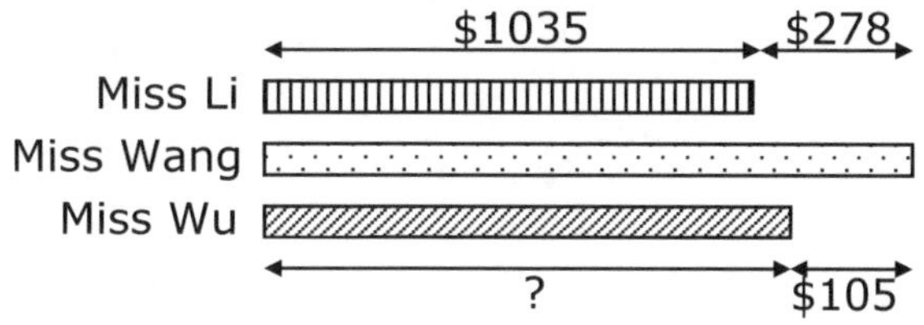

Practice 3A (p. 43)

1.	(a) 12	(b) 8	(c) 0	(d) 5
2.	(a) 30	(b) 7	(c) 20	(d) 0
3.	(a) 0	(b) 9	(c) 36	(d) 9

4. Total strawberries = 3 x 8 = **24**
5. Number of soldiers in each row = 24 ÷ 4 = **6**
6. Total amount saved = \$5 x 8 = **\$40**
7. Cost of 1 kg = \$18 ÷ 3 = **\$6**
8. Total number = 6 x 10 = **60**
9. Total paid = 4 x \$3 = **\$12**
10. Number of desks each boy cleaned = 27 ÷ 3 = **9**
11. Number of cards each child made = 24 ÷ 3 = **8**

Practice 3B (p. 47)

1.	(a) 12	(b) 8	(c) 14	(d) 8
2.	(a) 21	(b) 7	(c) 30	(d) 4
3.	(a) 12	(b) 5	(c) 32	(d) 7
4.	(a) 35	(b) 4	(c) 20	(d) 6
5.	(a) 90	(b) 7	(c) 27	(d) 9

6. Number of chairs in each row = 30 ÷ 6 = **5**

7. Cost of train set = $6 x 5 = **$30**

8. Total paid = 10 x $8 = **$80**

9. Weight of brother = 36 kg ÷ 4 = **9 kg**

10. (a) Number of pencils in each box = 5 + 3 = **8**
    (b) Total number of pencils = 8 x 4 = **32**

11. (a) number graded in a.m.
    = 8 x 5 = **40**
    (b) total graded
    = 40 + 30 = **70**

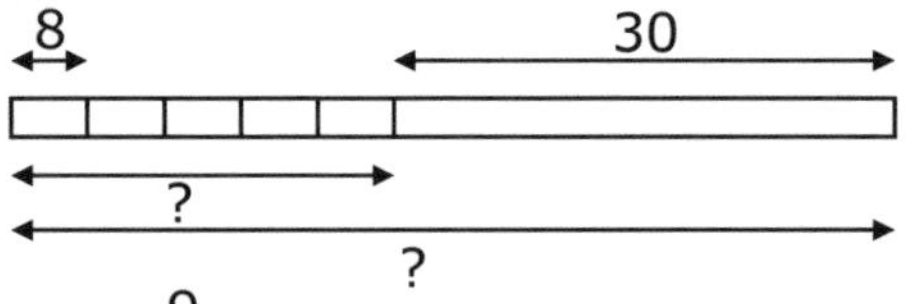

12. 1 unit = 9
    total units = 4
    Total balloons = 4 x 9 = 36
    Or: Number of blue balloons = 3 x 9 = 27
    Total balloons = 27 + 9 = **36**

Practice 3C (p. 48)

1.	(a) 5	(b) 7	(c) 18	(d) 7
2.	(a) 18	(b) 3	(c) 35	(d) 8
3.	(a) 9	(b) 0	(c) 24	(d) 5
4.	(a) 32	(b) 9	(c) 0	(d) 7
5.	(a) 0	(b) 7	(c) 24	(d) 0

6. Total money earned = $10 x 7 = **$70**

7. Amount of sugar = 15 kg ÷ 3 = **5 kg**

8. Total hours = 2 x 7 = **14**

3d➤9. Amount in each bottle = 16 ÷ 4 = **4** ℓ
US➤9. Amount in each bottle = 16 ÷ 4 = **4 quarts**

10. She has 2 units more.
    1 unit = 6
    2 units = 6 x 2 = **12**

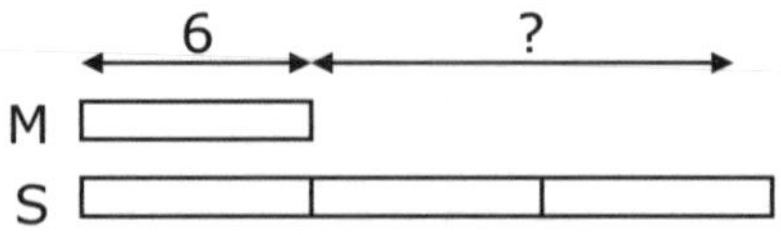

11. 1 unit = 6
    Total number of guppies = 6 x 5 = 30
    Number in each tank = 30 ÷ 3 = **10**

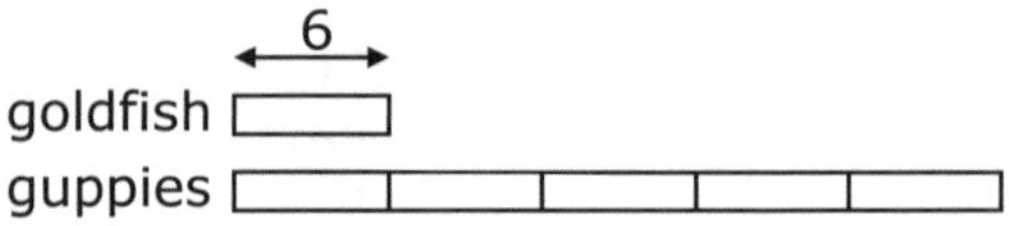

12. Total pens = 18 ÷ 2 = 9
    Cost of pens = 9 x $3 = **$27**

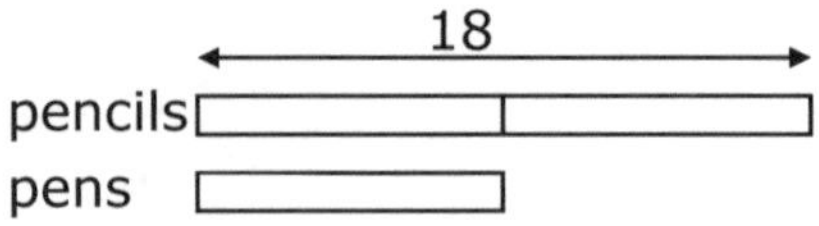

Practice 3D (p. 54)

1. (a) 180 (b) 240 (c) 2000 (d) 1000
2. (a) 240 (b) 50 (c) 4000 (d) 1600
3. (a) 100 (b) 120 (c) 800 (d) 1500
4. (a) 240 (b) 300 (c) 1200 (d) 2800
5. (a) 240 (b) 180 (c) 2800 (d) 2000
6. (a) 96 (b) 288 (c) 260 (d) 116
7. (a) 98 (b) 172 (c) 225 (d) 215
8. Books sold on second day = 30 x 8 = **240**
9. Total pictures = 24 x 4 = **96**
10. Total number of tiles = 56 x 5 = **280**
11. Number to stickers Sulin collected = 76 x 3 = **228**
12. Total amount she paid = 4 x $38 = **$152**

Practice 3E (p. 55)

1. (a) 1200 (b) 936 (c) 2095 (d) 2200
2. (a) 1802 (b) 1524 (c) 2500 (d) 1960
3. (a) 3070 (b) 1728 (c) 3905 (d) 1869
4. (a) 4000 (b) 1012 (c) 1756 (d) 2780
5. (a) 747 (b) 1805 (c) 3872 (d) 1408
6. Total number of pins = 126 x 3 = **378**
7. Cost of television set = $262 x 4 = **$1048**
8. Total number of beads = 260 x 3 = **780**
9. Total weight = 250 g x 5 = **1250 g**
10. Total eggs sold = 680 x 5 = **3400**
    or: Eggs sold this week = 680 x 4 = 2720
    Total eggs sold = 2720 + 680 = 3400

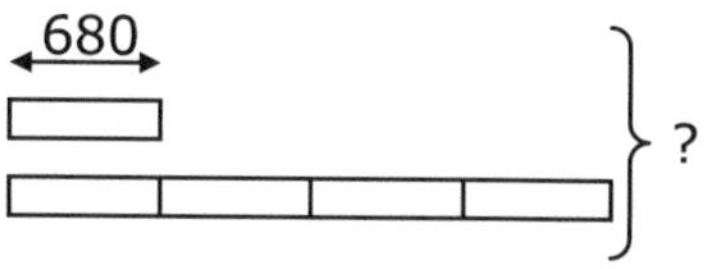

11. Total cost = $150 x 6 = **$900**
    or: Cost of refrigerator = $150 x 5 = $750
    Cost of both = $750 + $150 = $900

Practice 3F (p. 56)

1.	(a) 24	(b) 42	(c) 80	(d) 72
2.	(a) 446	(b) 2108	(c) 258	(d) 978
3.	(a) 756	(b) 3052	(c) 1860	(d) 852
4.	(a) 1448	(b) 315	(c) 1656	(d) 600
5.	(a) 780	(b) 2075	(c) 2545	(d) 1236

6. Number of chicken sandwiches = 280 x 3 = **840**
7. Number of days in 4 years = 365 x 4 = **1460**
8. Hours flown in 5 months = 105 x 5 = **525**
9. Weight of 2 boxes = 350 g x 2 = **700 g**
10. Total number of cakes = 30 x 4 = 120
    Total cost of cakes = 120 x $3 = **$360**
11. Number of chairs in 5 rows = 25 x 5 = 125
    Number of chairs in all rows = 125 + 18 = **143**

Practice 3G (p. 65)

1.	(a) 41	(b) 19 r1	(c) 76	(d) 16
2.	(a) 22 r3	(b) 15	(c) 12 r1	(d) 15 r2
3.	(a) 96	(b) 175 r2	(c) 59 r4	(d) 85 r4
4.	(a) 200	(b) 426 r1	(c) 82 r2	(d) 167
5.	(a) 149	(b) 225	(c) 137 r2	(d) 30 r3

6. 205 ÷ 4 = **51** r**1**
7. Weight of each packet = 750 ÷ 5 = **150 g**
8. 316 ÷ 3 = **105** r**1**
9. 74 ÷ 4 = **18** r**2**
10. Number of pieces = 429 ÷ 3 = **143**

Practice 3H (p. 66)

1.	(a) 100	(b) 21	(c) 204	(d) 25
2.	(a) 111	(b) 10	(c) 156	(d) 12
3.	(a) 1248	(b) 41	(c) 2500	(d) 102
4.	(a) 3455	(b) 67 r2	(c) 1821	(d) 166 r2
5.	(a) 2304	(b) 135 r4	(c) 3525	(d) 65 r3

6. Number of cows = 64 x 5 = **320**
7. (a) Hours worked in 26 days = 26 x 4 = **104**
   (b) Money earned = 104 x $3 = **$312**
8. Number of Malaysian stamps each gets = 150 ÷ 5 = **30**
   Number of Indonesian stamps each gets = 200 ÷ 5 = **40**
9. Number of bags = 215 ÷ 5 = 43
   Money received = 43 x $2 = **$86**
10. Cost of 4 balls = $18 x 4 = $72
    Money he still needs = $72 - $55 = **$17**

Review A (p. 67)

1. (a) 1970 (b) 5463 (c) 10,000
2. (a) 3645 (b) 2317 (c) 1
3. (a) 141 (b) 1035 (c) 3156
4. (a) 26 (b) 175 (c) 90 r1
5. Total number of children = 1628 + 1092 = **2720**
6. Number of tickets left = 4525 - 1909 = **2616**

US➤7. Number of gallons in 4 drums = 465 gal x 4 = **1940 gal.**
3d➤7. Number of liters in 4 drums = 485 l x 4 = **1940** ℓ

US➤8. (a) 563 ÷ 3 = 187 r2 Number of dresses made = **187**, cloth left = **2 yd**
(b) Money received = 187 x $5 = **$935**
3d➤8. (a) 563 ÷ 3 = 187 r2 Number of dresses made = **187**, cloth left = **2 m**
(b) Money received = 187 x $5 = **$935**

9. Number left = 1052 - 650 = 402
US➤ Number chapter books = 402 - 226 = **176**
3d➤ Number of children = 402 - 226 = **176**

10. Total money = $240 x 5 = **$960**
    or: Meilin's money = $240 x 3 = $720
    Total money = $720 + $240 = $960

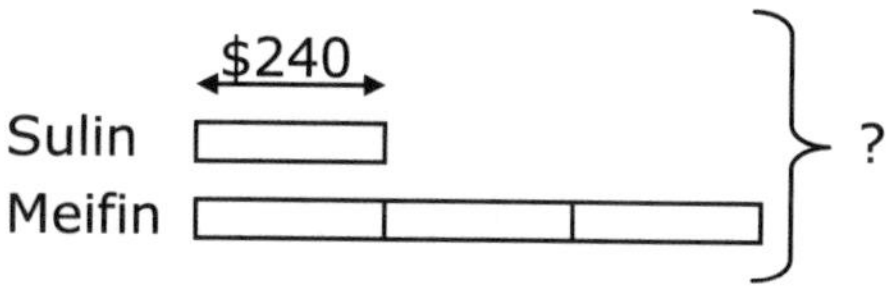

Practice 4A (p. 75)

1. (a) 18 (b) 24 (c) 42
2. (a) 3 (b) 4 (c) 7
3. (a) 258 (b) 564 (c) 342
4. (a) 13 r2 (b) 67 r3 (c) 93 r4
5. (a) 6 (b) 6 (c) 6 (d) 10
6. Number of players on 14 teams = 14 x 6 = **84**
7. Number each child gets = 84 ÷ 6 = **14**
8. Amount of money earned in 6 weeks = $85 x 6 = **$510**
9. Number of bundles = 192 ÷ 6 = **32**
10. Cost of 1 m of cloth = $84 ÷ 6 = $14
    Cost of 5 m of cloth = $14 x 5 = **$70**
    or: Cost of 5 m of cloth = cost of 6 m – cost of 1 m = $84 – $14 = $70
11. Amount he must pay = 6 x $6 = **$36**

Practice 4B (p. 80)

1. (a) 28 (b) 42 (c) 21 (d) 63
2. (a) 4 (b) 6 (c) 3 (d) 9
3. (a) 280 (b) 4256 (c) 5600 (d) 6510
4. (a) 13 r4 (b) 77 r1 (c) 102 (d) 115
5. 150 ÷ 7 = 21 r 3 He will bake **21** cakes and have **3** eggs left over.
6. Number of days in 52 weeks = 52 x 7 = **364**
7. Age of grandson = 63 ÷ 7 = **9**
8. Amount she paid = $26 x 7 = **$182**
9. Cost of 1 towel = $84 ÷ 7 = **$12**
10. Number of bags = 112 ÷ 7 = 16
    Money received = 16 x $3 = **$48**
11. Cost of jacket = $26 x 7 = $182
    Cost of both = $182 + $26 = **$208**

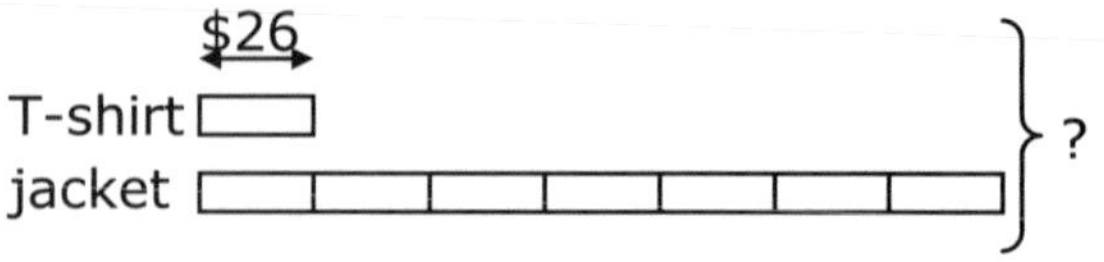

Practice 4C (p. 81)

1. (a) 36 (b) 56 (c) 60 (d) 49
2. (a) 6 (b) 7 (c) 10 (d) 7
3. (a) 469 (b) 0 (c) 10 (d) 3591
4. (a) 50 r4 (b) 0 (c) 1 (d) 121

US➤5. Length of each piece = 161 in. ÷ 7 = **23 in.**
3d➤5. Length of each piece = 161 cm ÷ 7 = **23 cm**

6. Amount he spent = 28 x $6 = **$168**
7. Number of cakes = 84 ÷ 6 = **14**
8. Total cookies = 48 x 3 = 144
   Number of cookies each child got = 144 ÷ 6 = **24**
9. Total number of pens = 12 x 7 = 84
   Number of blue pens = 84 – 36 = **48**

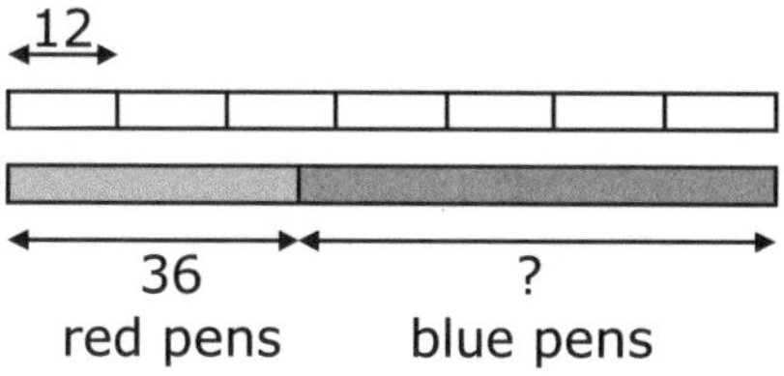

10. Total spent = 35 x $6 = $210
    Money she started with = $25 + $210 = **$235**

Practice 4D (p. 84)

1. (a) 24 (b) 48 (c) 80 (d) 64
2. (a) 3 (b) 7 (c) 10 (d) 8
3. (a) 344 (b) 776 (c) 2096 (d) 6992
4. (a) 15 (b) 72 r3 (c) 93 r1 (d) 104
5. (a) 4 (b) 6 (c) 8 (d) 9
6. Total number of people = 36 x 8 = **288**
7. Amount of water tank holds = 18ℓ x 8 = **144ℓ**
8. 390 ÷ 8 = 48 r6 She had **48** packets, with **6** tarts left over.
9. Cost of 12 cans = 12 x $8 = $96
   Change = $100 – $96 = **$4**
10. Monthly payments
    = $103 x 8 = $824
    Total cost
    = $245 + $824 = **$1069**

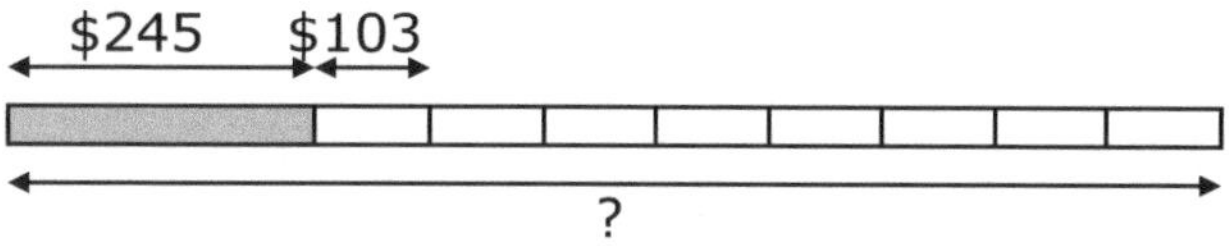

Practice 4E (p. 85)

1.	(a) 42	(b) 56	(c) 80	(d) 72
2.	(a) 7	(b) 8	(c) 6	(d) 9
3.	(a)10 r3	(b) 8	(c) 0	(d) 18 r6
4.	(a) 117 r7	(b) 8	(c) 0	(d) 145 r2

5. 145 ÷ 6 = 24 r1 There were **24** packets, with **1 kg** of sugar left over.
6. Number of umbrellas he can buy = \$168 ÷ \$7 = **24**
7. Total pages in 8 books = 120 x 8 = **960**
8. Cost of chairs = 6 x \$28 = \$168
   Money still needed = \$168 – \$100 = **\$68**
9. Cost for boat = \$12 x 6 = \$72
   Cost for each person = \$72 ÷ 8 = **\$9**

Practice 4F (p. 89)

1.	(a) 27	(b) 36	(c) 45	(d) 81
2.	(a) 3	(b) 4	(c) 5	(d) 9
3.	(a) 324	(b) 3600	(c) 5913	(d) 1782
4.	(a) 106	(b) 62 r5	(c) 87 r7	(d) 91 r4

5. Total meters bought = 9 x 18 m = **162 m**
6. Total number of cans = 25 x 9 = **225**
7. Cost of 1 T-shirt = \$144 ÷ 9 = **\$16**
8. Number of pieces = 918 m ÷ 9 m = **102**
9. Amount used in 9 months = 185 ℓ x 9 = **1665** ℓ
10. Total number of buttons = 120 x 9 = 1080
    Number of dresses = 1080 ÷ 8 = **135**
11. Cost of a group of 3 apples is \$2. Find the number of groups of 3 apples.
    Number of groups of 3 apples = 27 ÷ 3 = 9
    Total cost = number of groups of 3 x \$2 = 9 x \$2 = **\$18**

Practice 4G (p. 90)

1.	(a) 54	(b) 70	(c) 64	(d) 36
2.	(a) 9	(b) 10	(c) 8	(d) 6
3.	(a) 552	(b) 9	(c) 0	(d) 5406
4.	(a) 64 r5	(b) 9	(c) 0	(d) 107

5. Number of children = $28 ÷ $7 = **4**
6. Number of buckets needed to fill the tank = 126 ÷ 9 = **14**
7. Total money received = $36 x 7 = **$252**
8. Number of sunflowers = 136 x 6 = **816**
8. Number of good tomatoes = 112 - 8 = 104
   Number of packets = 104 ÷ 8 = **13**
10. Total stamps = 120 x 8 = 960
    Number sold = 960 - 680 = **280**

Practice 5A (p. 93)

1. (a) 20¢ (b) 65¢ (c) 700¢
   (d) 205¢ (e) 560¢ (f) 395¢
2. (a) $0.05 (b) $0.60 (c) $4.00
   (d) $2.10 (e) $8.55 (f) $3.05
3. (a) 70¢ (b) 55¢ (c) 60¢ (d) 35¢

US➤4. (a) $1.50 (b) $0.60 (c) $2.10
3d➤4. (a) $1.20 (b) $0.60 (c) $1.80

5. $4.70

Practice 5B (p. 102)

1. (a) $39.70 (b) $100.00
   (c) $75.70 (d) $40.30
   (e) $91.65 (f) $91.00
2. (a) $21.35 (b) $36.05
   (c) $21.60 (d) $23.75
   (e) $45.25 (f) $49.15
3. Total money = $24.60 + $76.40 = **$101.00**
4. Additional money needed = $62.50 - $48.60 = **$13.90**
5. Cost of toy airplane = $16.80 + $5.60 = **$22.40**
6. Cost of lunch = $10 - $6.95 = **$3.05**
7. Cost of skirt = $42.50 - $16.85 = **$25.65**
8. Total spent = $6.80 + $13.20 = $20
   Money left = $40.50 - $20.00 = **$20.50**

Practice 5C (p. 103)

1. (a) \$41.00 (b) \$3.25
2. (a) \$30.60 (b) \$25.15
3. (a) \$100.00 (b) \$18.95
4. (a) \$63.40 (b) \$9.10
5. (a) \$99.90 (b) \$28.30
6. Amount badminton racket is cheaper = \$42.50 – \$15.90 = **\$26.60**
7. Amount radio is cheaper at sale price = \$43 – \$29.95 = **\$13.05**
8. Amount her mother gave her = \$12.30 – \$10.80 = **\$1.50**
9. Total spent = \$2.40 + \$3.70 = \$6.10
   Total money = \$21.30 + \$6.10 = **\$27.40**
10. Cost of duck = \$5.70 + \$1.95 = \$7.65
    Total cost = \$7.65 + \$5.70 = **\$13.35**

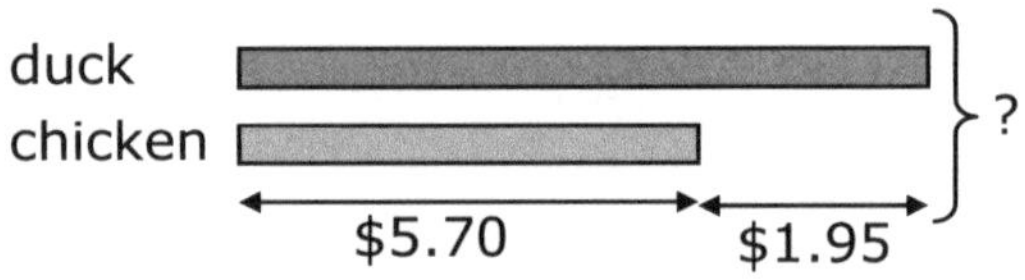

Review B (p.104)

1. (a) 701 (b) 1110 (c) 5000
2. (a) 702 (b) 609 (c) 909
3. (a) 294 (b) 1428 (c) 3438
4. (a) 16 (b) 14 r6 (c) 32 r4
5. Total amount earned = \$45 x 9 = **\$405**

US➤6. Cost of each dress = \$56 ÷ 4 = **\$14**
3d➤6. Number of kg bought = \$56 ÷ \$4 = **14 kg**

7. Amount by which father is heavier
   = 2 x 29 kg = **58 kg**

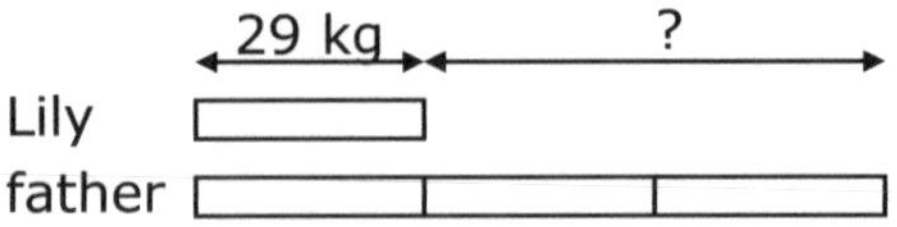

8. Total number of tiles used = 1164 + 940 = 2104
   Number of tiles left = 2500 – 2104 = **396**
9. Cost of present = \$100 – \$48 = \$52
   Amount each person paid = \$52 ÷ 4 = **\$13**
10. Total = 12 x 8 = 96
    Amount eaten = 96 – 28 = **68**

Mental Math 1			
1.	43	16.	131
2.	244	17.	85
3.	378	18.	510
4.	51	19.	457
5.	146	20.	34
6.	240	21.	462
7.	172	22.	570
8.	222	23.	46
9.	121	24.	171
10.	220	25.	341
11.	155	26.	532
12.	85	27.	115
13.	145	28.	510
14.	103	29.	60
15.	72	30.	883

Mental Math 2			
1.	42	16.	885
2.	360	17.	19
3.	687	18.	233
4.	261	19.	31
5.	77	20.	70
6.	43	21.	370
7.	95	22.	648
8.	553	23.	254
9.	221	24.	61
10.	79	25.	840
11.	126	26.	54
12.	450	27.	880
13.	83	28.	26
14.	45	29.	492
15.	22	30.	791

Mental Math 3			
1.	858	16.	3502
2.	3688	17.	8864
3.	1200	18.	384
4.	6632	19.	6064
5.	8942	20.	870
6.	8303	21.	5300
7.	6312	22.	3653
8.	9774	23.	6588
9.	888	24.	4742
10.	410	25.	731
11.	5730	26.	6321
12.	333	27.	6400
13.	7741	28.	930
14.	3468	29.	589
15.	6588	30.	4240

Mental Math 4			
1.	47	16.	530
2.	7281	17.	609
3.	121	18.	3720
4.	79	19.	690
5.	395	20.	4233
6.	78	21.	52
7.	4301	22.	606
8.	8301	23.	820
9.	508	24.	503
10.	262	25.	300
11.	10,000	26.	179
12.	7051	27.	100
13.	8239	28.	1224
14.	9776	29.	7262
15.	25	30.	9000

Mental Math 5			
1.	3589	16.	3008
2.	6884	17.	3698
3.	8776	18.	3925
4.	8937	19.	7020
5.	2865	20.	3664
6.	1287	21.	3823
7.	6899	22.	7063
8.	7552	23.	2068
9.	4697	24.	3699
10.	2799	25.	5123
11.	9386	26.	6348
12.	9898	27.	6796
13.	6952	28.	9999
14.	2008	29.	2677
15.	5555	30.	6870

Mental Math 6			
1.	2566	16.	2690
2.	2110	17.	2990
3.	2111	18.	3990
4.	2113	19.	6610
5.	1100	20.	7610
6.	4100	21.	7611
7.	4106	22.	4121
8.	4116	23.	4141
9.	4118	24.	4145
10.	4168	25.	1500
11.	5533	26.	1556
12.	5534	27.	2500
13.	6534	28.	2556
14.	6314	29.	3098
15.	6414	30.	6815

Mental Math 7			
1.	5623	16.	9873
2.	3638	17.	9853
3.	5542	18.	9351
4.	4698	19.	6351
5.	6301	20.	9500
6.	3247	21.	352
7.	5894	22.	6226
8.	9123	23.	95
9.	2222	24.	68
10.	8642	25.	398
11.	3128	26.	7398
12.	644	27.	4698
13.	730	28.	4488
14.	736	29.	356
15.	675	30.	275

Mental Math 8			
1.	8215	16.	4900
2.	8150	17.	4906
3.	7500	18.	4966
4.	1000	19.	4965
5.	8156	20.	4945
6.	8154	21.	6116
7.	7564	22.	6053
8.	7554	23.	5423
9.	7551	24.	2111
10.	5357	25.	6573
11.	9774	26.	2530
12.	9773	27.	2582
13.	8964	28.	5600
14.	8941	29.	5685
15.	634	30.	203

Mental Math 9			
1.	853	16.	377
2.	733	17.	518
3.	367	18.	254
4.	504	19.	449
5.	733	20.	600
6.	4324	21.	700
7.	3364	22.	977
8.	8167	23.	911
9.	3164	24.	692
10.	173	25.	68
11.	408	26.	103
12.	571	27.	3928
13.	209	28.	5380
14.	8865	29.	8388
15.	5002	30.	9568

Mental Math 10										
x	5	3	6	1	4	10	2	9	8	7
3	15	9	18	3	12	30	6	27	24	21
10	50	30	60	10	40	100	20	90	80	70
2	10	6	12	2	8	20	4	18	16	14
5	25	15	30	5	20	50	10	45	40	35
4	20	12	24	4	16	40	8	36	32	28
x	4	10	9	6	2	7	3	8	1	5
4	16	40	36	24	8	28	12	32	4	20
5	20	50	45	30	10	35	15	40	5	25
3	12	30	27	18	6	21	9	24	3	15
10	40	100	90	60	20	70	30	80	10	50
2	8	20	18	12	4	14	6	16	2	10

Mental Math 11			
1.	4	16.	30
2.	25	17.	30
3.	12	18.	12
4.	20	19.	9
5.	50	20.	16
6.	10	21.	0
7.	21	22.	15
8.	45	23.	8
9.	14	24.	24
10.	40	25.	24
11.	20	26.	0
12.	35	27.	27
13.	28	28.	16
14.	18	29.	18
15.	36	30.	32

Mental Math 12			
1.	10	16.	8
2.	4	17.	10
3.	8	18.	7
4.	10	19.	3
5.	4	20.	1
6.	4	21.	5
7.	6	22.	5
8.	1	23.	7
9.	3	24.	5
10.	6	25.	15
11.	1	26.	5
12.	9	27.	7
13.	7	28.	2
14.	9	29.	8
15.	6	30.	1

Mental Math 13			
1.	7	16.	32
2.	21	17.	3
3.	2	18.	90
4.	3	19.	24
5.	60	20.	1
6.	8	21.	45
7.	35	22.	9
8.	9	23.	0
9.	70	24.	2
10.	36	25.	40
11.	24	26.	10
12.	18	27.	30
13.	4	28.	8
14.	0	29.	28
15.	27	30.	10

Mental Math 14			
1.	4500	16.	3200
2.	1200	17.	100
3.	280	18.	2700
4.	1200	19.	400
5.	3500	20.	180
6.	140	21.	2000
7.	1600	22.	150
8.	240	23.	800
9.	360	24.	3000
10.	90	25.	1600
11.	250	26.	2100
12.	4000	27.	120
13.	1800	28.	2400
14.	200	29.	40
15.	4000	30.	5000

Mental Math 15			
1.	6442	16.	2957
2.	433	17.	270
3.	20	18.	244
4.	175	19.	2820
5.	9	20.	9777
6.	1600	21.	2400
7.	736	22.	1800
8.	2514	23.	5065
9.	240	24.	100
10.	665	25.	18
11.	25	26.	6438
12.	2435	27.	139
13.	1681	28.	3300
14.	667	29.	45
15.	7	30.	2400

Mental Math 16			
1.	50	16.	162
2.	75	17.	106
3.	100	18.	36
4.	40	19.	58
5.	60	20.	92
6.	80	21.	32
7.	100	22.	48
8.	24	23.	12
9.	36	24.	24
10.	48	25.	12
11.	60	26.	24
12.	72	27.	32
13.	84	28.	64
14.	96	29.	128
15.	108	30.	256

Mental Math 18			
1.	231		
2.	150 + 20 = 170		
3.	160 + 14 = 174		
4.	160 + 12 = 172		
5.	120 + 15 = 135		
6.	425	16.	320
7.	124	17.	141
8.	165	18.	124
9.	129	19.	138
10.	252	20.	84
11.	46	21.	410
12.	168	22.	196
13.	180	23.	72
14.	142	24.	249
15.	84	25.	135

Mental Math 19			
1.	18	16.	6
2.	60	17.	8
3.	36	18.	6
4.	54	19.	1
5.	48	20.	3
6.	12	21.	4
7.	30	22.	7
8.	20	23.	5
9.	42	24.	9
10.	32	25.	7
11.	24	26.	10
12.	0	27.	4
13.	21	28.	7
14.	54	29.	9
15.	42	30.	9

Mental Math 20			
1.	42	16.	8
2.	63	17.	6
3.	54	18.	8
4.	56	19.	7
5.	35	20.	4
6.	56	21.	2
7.	42	22.	1
8.	28	23.	3
9.	36	24.	5
10.	35	25.	6
11.	63	26.	7
12.	48	27.	9
13.	49	28.	5
14.	343	29.	9
15.	546	30.	7

Mental Math 21			
1.	72	16.	6
2.	40	17.	8
3.	64	18.	9
4.	48	19.	5
5.	40	20.	7
6.	32	21.	4
7.	56	22.	6
8.	64	23.	9
9.	42	24.	8
10.	48	25.	7
11.	56	26.	6
12.	36	27.	8
13.	49	28.	3
14.	344	29.	8
15.	656	30.	2

Mental Math 22			
1.	54	16.	6
2.	49	17.	9
3.	81	18.	7
4.	63	19.	9
5.	64	20.	8
6.	45	21.	5
7.	72	22.	6
8.	54	23.	6
9.	63	24.	9
10.	27	25.	7
11.	36	26.	3
12.	36	27.	7
13.	72	28.	9
14.	558	29.	4
15.	189	30.	8

Mental Math 23			
1.	72	16.	6
2.	6	17.	8
3.	5	18.	6
4.	63	19.	6
5.	48	20.	7
6.	9	21.	81
7.	42	22.	5
8.	8	23.	64
9.	63	24.	49
10.	72	25.	54
11.	9	26.	9
12.	7	27.	56
13.	7	28.	7
14.	8	29.	9
15.	42	30.	56

Mental Math 24

x	4	9	6	2	7	3	8	5
6	24	54	36	12	42	18	48	30
7	28	63	42	14	49	21	56	35
8	32	72	48	16	56	24	64	40
9	36	81	54	18	63	27	72	45

x	5	7	4	6	2	3	9	8
8	40	56	32	48	16	24	72	64
7	35	49	28	42	14	21	63	56
9	45	63	36	54	18	27	81	72
6	40	42	24	36	12	18	54	48

x	2	7	3	6	4	5	9	8
9	18	63	27	54	36	45	81	72
7	14	49	21	42	28	35	63	56
8	16	56	24	48	32	40	72	64
6	12	42	18	36	24	30	54	48

Mental Math 25			
1.	348	16.	9757
2.	533	17.	8
3.	9	18.	744
4.	3742	19.	99
5.	48	20.	168
6.	999	21.	810
7.	2720	22.	1443
8.	8	23.	6400
9.	208	24.	3157
10.	736	25.	540
11.	5600	26.	9
12.	3160	27.	568
13.	4768	28.	4547
14.	8	29.	958
15.	420	30.	3500

This page is blank.

Mental Math 1

1. 37 + 6 = ________
2. 238 + 6 = ________
3. 369 + 9 = ________
4. 46 + 5 = ________
5. 96 + 50 = ________
6. 160 + 80 = ________
7. 92 + 80 = ________
8. 142 + 80 = ________
9. 91 + 30 = ________
10. 160 + 60 = ________
11. 62 + 93 = ________
12. 81 + 4 = ________
13. 65 + 80 = ________
14. 81 + 22 = ________
15. 3 + 69 = ________
16. 41 + 90 = ________
17. 78 + 7 = ________
18. 490 + 20 = ________
19. 448 + 9 = ________
20. 27 + 7 = ________
21. 382 + 80 = ________
22. 569 + 1 = ________
23. 39 + 7 = ________
24. 167 + 4 = ________
25. 251 + 90 = ________
26. 482 + 50 = ________
27. 109 + 6 = ________
28. 480 + 30 = ________
29. 27 + 33= ________
30. 9 + 874 = ________

Mental Math 2

1. 51 – 9 = __________
2. 420 – 60 = __________
3. 693 – 6 = __________
4. 351 – 90 = __________
5. 82 – 5 = __________
6. 49 – 6 = __________
7. 100 – 5 = __________
8. 623 – 70 = __________
9. 230 – 9 = __________
10. 82 – 3 = __________
11. 134 – 8 = __________
12. 510 – 60 = __________
13. 92 – 9 = __________
14. 54 – 9 = __________
15. 59 – 37 = __________
16. 892 – 7 = __________
17. 24 – 5 = __________
18. 241 – 8 = __________
19. 38 – 7 = __________
20. 140 – 70 = __________
21. 410 – 40 = __________
22. 653 – 5 = __________
23. 334 – 80 = __________
24. 91 – 30 = __________
25. 920 – 80 = __________
26. 61 – 7 = __________
27. 920 – 40 = __________
28. 30 – 4 = __________
29. 500 – 8 = __________
30. 811 – 20 = __________

Mental Math 3

1. 158 + 700 = __________
2. 3687 + 1 = __________
3. 700 + 500 = __________
4. 100 + 6532 = __________
5. 8952 – 10 = __________
6. 8304 – 1 = __________
7. 6212 + 100 = __________
8. 9874 – 100 = __________
9. 237 + 651 = __________
10. 870 – 460 = __________
11. 5731 – 1 = __________
12. 984 – 651 = __________
13. 8741 – 1000 = __________
14. 3478 – 10 = __________
15. 6587 + 1 = __________
16. 3002 + 500 = __________
17. 1000 + 7864 = __________
18. 684 – 300 = __________
19. 6054 + 10 = __________
20. 250 + 620 = __________
21. 5200 + 100 = __________
22. 3654 – 1 = __________
23. 1 + 6587 = __________
24. 4752 – 10 = __________
25. 700 + 31 = __________
26. 6421 – 100 = __________
27. 5400 + 1000 = __________
28. 420 + 510 = __________
29. 532 + 57 = __________
30. 3240 + 1000 = __________

Mental Math 4

1. 38 + 9 = ________
2. 6281 + 1000 = ________
3. 100 + 21 = ________
4. 62 + 17 = ________
5. 399 – 4 = ________
6. 84 – 6 = ________
7. 4300 + 1 = ________
8. 8201 + 100 = ________
9. 438 + 70 = ________
10. 322 – 60 = ________
11. 9000 + 1000 = ________
12. 6951 + 100 = ________
13. 8229 + 10 = ________
14. 9777 – 1 = ________
15. 100 – 75 = ________
16. 470 + 60 = ________
17. 604 + 5 = ________
18. 3820 – 100 = ________
19. 687 + 3 = ________
20. 4333 – 100 = ________
21. 75 – 23 = ________
22. 526 + 80 = ________
23. 910 – 90 = ________
24. 512 – 9 = ________
25. 360 – 60 = ________
26. 259 – 80 = ________
27. 35 + 65 = ________
28. 1234 – 10 = ________
29. 8262 – 1000 = ________
30. 10,000 – 1000 = ________

Mental Math 5

1. 3587 + 2 = ________
2. 6834 + 50 = ________
3. 8476 + 300 = ________
4. 2937 + 6000 = ________
5. 2565 + 300 = ________
6. 1284 + 3 = ________
7. 6829 + 70 = ________
8. 4552 + 3000 = ________
9. 4632 + 65 = ________
10. 2568 + 231 = ________
11. 3125 + 6261 = ________
12. 62 + 9836 = ________
13. 430 + 6522 = ________
14. 6 + 2002 = ________
15. 2552 + 3003 = ________
16. 3005 + 3 = ________
17. 3658 + 40 = ________
18. 3025 + 900 = ________
19. 3020 + 4000 = ________
20. 3634 + 30 = ________
21. 3123 + 700 = ________
22. 2063 + 5000 = ________
23. 2063 + 5 = ________
24. 8 + 3691 = ________
25. 3000 + 2123 = ________
26. 28 + 6320 = ________
27. 625 + 6171 = ________
28. 8008 + 1991 = ________
29. 2654 + 23 = ________
30. 6510 + 360 = ________

Mental Math 6

1. 2559 + 7 = ________
2. 2060 + 50 = ________
3. 2061 + 50 = ________
4. 2061 + 52 = ________
5. 700 + 400 = ________
6. 3700 + 400 = ________
7. 3706 + 400 = ________
8. 3716 + 400 = ________
9. 3716 + 402 = ________
10. 3716 + 452 = ________
11. 5463 + 70 = ________
12. 5463 + 71 = ________
13. 5463 + 1071 = ________
14. 6308 + 6 = ________
15. 6308 + 106 = ________
16. 2684 + 6 = ________
17. 2684 + 306 = ________
18. 2684 + 1306 = ________
19. 6540 + 70 = ________
20. 6540 + 1070 = ________
21. 6540 + 1071 = ________
22. 3521 + 600 = ________
23. 3521 + 620 = ________
24. 3521 + 624 = ________
25. 600 + 900 = ________
26. 625 + 931 = ________
27. 1600 + 900 = ________
28. 1625 + 931 = ________
29. 2785 + 313 = ________
30. 6781 + 34 = ________

Mental Math 7

1. 5629 – 6 = ________
2. 3658 – 20 = ________
3. 5842 – 300 = ________
4. 6698 – 2000 = ________
5. 6306 – 5 = ________
6. 3269 – 22 = ________
7. 6214 – 320 = ________
8. 9586 – 463 = ________
9. 6852 – 4630 = ________
10. 9876 – 1234 = ________
11. 9999 – 6871 = ________
12. 652 – 8 = ________
13. 820 – 90 = ________
14. 986 – 250 = ________
15. 682 – 7 = ________
16. 9874 – 1 = ________
17. 9874 – 21 = ________
18. 9872 – 521 = ________
19. 9872 – 3521 = ________
20. 10,000 – 500 = ________
21. 652 – 300 = ________
22. 6526 – 300 = ________
23. 98 – 3 = ________
24. 98 – 30 = ________
25. 698 – 300 = ________
26. 7698 – 300 = ________
27. 7698 – 3000 = ________
28. 7698 – 3210 = ________
29. 365 – 9 = ________
30. 365 – 90 = ________

Mental Math 8

1. 8222 – 7 = 8215
2. 8220 – 70 = 8150
3. 8200 – 700 = 7500
4. 8000 – 7000 = 1000
5. 8226 – 70 = 8156
6. 8226 – 72 = 8154
7. 8264 – 700 = 7564
8. 8264 – 710 = 7554
9. 8264 – 713 = ________
10. 5365 – 8 = 5357
11. 9864 – 90 = 9774
12. 9864 – 91 = ________
13. 9864 – 900 = ________
14. 9864 – 923 = ________
15. 9864 – 9230 = ________
16. 5400 – 500 = 4900
17. 5406 – 500 = 4906
18. 5466 – 500 = ________
19. 5466 – 501 = ________
20. 5466 – 521 = ________
21. 6123 – 7 = ________
22. 6123 – 70 = ________
23. 6123 – 700 = ________
24. 6123 – 4012 = ________
25. 6582 – 9 = ________
26. 2600 – 70 = ________
27. 2654 – 72 = ________
28. 6200 – 600 = ________
29. 6287 – 602 = ________
30. 1103 – 900 = ________

Mental Math 9

1. 950 − 97 = ________
2. 638 + 95 = 733
3. 865 − 498 = ________
4. 105 + 399 = 504
5. 36 + 697 = ________
6. 4226 + 98 = 4324
7. 3269 + 95 = 3364
8. 8264 − 97 = ________
9. 3260 − 96 = ________
10. 268 − 95 = ________
11. 312 + 96 = ________
12. 868 − 297 = ________
13. 404 − 195 = ________
14. 9864 − 999 = ________
15. 4004 + 998 = 2002
16. 400 − 23 = ________
17. 600 − 82 = ________
18. 300 − 46 = ________
19. 500 − 51 = ________
20. 547 + 53 = ________
21. 612 + 88 = ________
22. 1000 − 23 = ________
23. 1000 − 89 = ________
24. 1000 − 308 = ________
25. 1000 − 932 = ________
26. 1000 − 897 = ________
27. 4000 − 72 = ________
28. 6000 − 620 = ________
29. 9000 − 612 = ________
30. 10,000 − 432 = ________

Mental Math 10

x	5	3	6	1	4	10	2	9	8	7
3										
10										
2										
5										
4										

x	4	10	9	6	2	7	3	8	1	5
4										
5										
3										
10										
2										

Mental Math 11

1. 2 x 2 = ________
2. 5 x 5 = ________
3. 4 x 3 = ________
4. 5 x 4 = ________
5. 10 x 5 = ________
6. 2 x 5 = ________
7. 3 x 7 = ________
8. 5 x 9 = ________
9. 2 x 7 = ________
10. 8 x 5 = ________
11. 10 x 2 = ________
12. 5 x 7 = ________
13. 7 x 4 = ________
14. 2 x 9 = ________
15. 9 x 4 = ________
16. 3 x 10 = ________
17. 6 x 5 = ________
18. 6 x 2 = ________
19. 3 x 3 = ________
20. 4 x 4 = ________
21. 0 x 3 = ________
22. 3 x 5 = ________
23. 4 x 2 = ________
24. 8 x 3 = ________
25. 4 x 6 = ________
26. 0 x 10 = ________
27. 9 x 3 = ________
28. 8 x 2 = ________
29. 6 x 3 = ________
30. 4 x 8 = ________

Mental Math 12

1. $50 \div 5 =$ ________
2. $12 \div 3 =$ ________
3. $24 \div 3 =$ ________
4. $20 \div 2 =$ ________
5. $20 \div 5 =$ ________
6. $8 \div 2 =$ ________
7. $24 \div 4 =$ ________
8. $10 \div 10 =$ ________
9. $15 \div 5 =$ ________
10. $18 \div 3 =$ ________
11. $4 \div 4 =$ ________
12. $27 \div 3 =$ ________
13. $14 \div 2 =$ ________
14. $36 \div 4 =$ ________
15. $12 \div 2 =$ ________
16. $16 \div 2 =$ ________
17. $40 \div 4 =$ ________
18. $21 \div 3 =$ ________
19. $6 \div 2 =$ ________
20. $5 \div 5 =$ ________
21. $10 \div 2 =$ ________
22. $25 \div 5 =$ ________
23. $28 \div 4 =$ ________
24. $15 \div 3 =$ ________
25. $30 \div 2 =$ ________
26. $20 \div 4 =$ ________
27. $70 \div 10 =$ ________
28. $8 \div 4 =$ ________
29. $40 \div 5 =$ ________
30. $3 \div 3 =$ ________

Mental Math 13

1. $35 \div 5 =$ ________
2. $7 \times 3 =$ ________
3. $4 \div 2 =$ ________
4. $12 \div 4 =$ ________
5. $10 \times 6 =$ ________
6. $80 \div 10 =$ ________
7. $5 \times 7 =$ ________
8. $45 \div 5 =$ ________
9. $7 \times 10 =$ ________
10. $4 \times 9 =$ ________
11. $3 \times 8 =$ ________
12. $9 \times 2 =$ ________
13. $16 \div 4 =$ ________
14. $0 \div 2 =$ ________
15. $9 \times 3 =$ ________
16. $8 \times 4 =$ ________
17. $9 \div 3 =$ ________
18. $10 \times 9 =$ ________
19. $6 \times 4 =$ ________
20. $5 \div 5 =$ ________
21. $9 \times 5 =$ ________
22. $18 \div 2 =$ ________
23. $0 \times 3 =$ ________
24. $10 \div 5 =$ ________
25. $8 \times 5 =$ ________
26. $30 \div 3 =$ ________
27. $6 \times 5 =$ ________
28. $32 \div 4 =$ ________
29. $4 \times 7 =$ ________
30. $100 \div 10 =$ ________

Mental Math 14

1. 900 x 5 = ________
2. 600 x 2 = ________
3. 70 x 4 = ________
4. 400 x 3 = ________
5. 5 x 700 = ________
6. 70 x 2 = ________
7. 400 x 4 = ________
8. 80 x 3 = ________
9. 90 x 4 = ________
10. 30 x 3 = ________
11. 50 x 5 = ________
12. 800 x 5 = ________
13. 600 x 3 = ________
14. 50 x 4 = ________
15. 1000 x 4 = ________
16. 800 x 4 = ________
17. 50 x 2 = ________
18. 900 x 3 = ________
19. 80 x 5 = ________
20. 90 x 2 = ________
21. 5 x 400 = ________
22. 50 x 3 = ________
23. 400 x 2 = ________
24. 600 x 5 = ________
25. 800 x 2 = ________
26. 3 x 700 = ________
27. 3 x 40 = ________
28. 4 x 600 = ________
29. 20 x 2 = ________
30. 1000 x 5 = ________

Mental Math 15

1. 6439 + 3 = ________
2. 363 + 70 = ________
3. 5 x 4 = ________
4. 265 - 90 = ________
5. 27 ÷ 3 = ________
6. 400 x 4 = ________
7. 986 – 250 = ________
8. 3000 – 486 = ________
9. 60 x 4 = ________
10. 569 + 96 = ________
11. 5 x 5 = ________
12. 1624 + 811 = ________
13. 1986 – 305 = ________
14. 368 + 299 = ________
15. 28 ÷ 4 = ________
16. 3056 – 99 = ________
17. 90 x 3 = ________
18. 300 – 56 = ________
19. 3520 – 700 = ________
20. 4135 + 5642 = ________
21. 2342 + 58 = ________
22. 2 x 900 = ________
23. 6000 – 935 = ________
24. 1000 ÷ 10 = ________
25. 3 x 6 = ________
26. 6800 – 362 = ________
27. 434 – 295 = ________
28. 3238 + 62 = ________
29. 9 x 5 = ________
30. 6 x 400 = ________

Mental Math 16

1. 25 x 2 = ________
2. 25 x 3 = ________
3. 25 x 4 = ________
4. 20 x 2 = ________
5. 20 x 3 = ________
6. 20 x 4 = ________
7. 20 x 5 = ________
8. 12 x 2 = ________
9. 12 x 3 = ________
10. 12 x 4 = ________
11. 12 x 5 = ________
12. 12 x 6 = ________
13. 12 x 7 = ________
14. 12 x 8 = ________
15. 12 x 9 = ________
16. 81 x 2 = ________
17. 53 x 2 = ________
18. 18 x 2 = ________
19. 29 x 2 = ________
20. 46 x 2 = ________
21. 16 x 2 = ________
22. 16 x 3 = ________
23. 24 ÷ 2 = ________
24. 48 ÷ 2 = ________
25. 36 ÷ 3 = ________
26. 48 ÷ 2 = ________
27. 16 x 2 = ________
28. 32 x 2 = ________
29. 64 x 2 = ________
30. 128 x 2 = ________

Mental Math 17

x	1	2	3	4	5	6	7	8	9	10
1										
2										
3										
4										
5										
6										
7										
8										
9										
10										

Mental Math 18

1. 77 x 3 = 210 + 21 = ________
2. 34 x 5 = ______ + _______ = __________
3. 87 x 2 = ______ + _______ = __________
4. 43 x 4 = ______ + _______ = __________
5. 45 x 3 = ______ + _______ = __________
6. 85 x 5 = ________
7. 62 x 2 = ________
8. 33 x 5 = ________
9. 43 x 3 = ________
10. 63 x 4 = ________
11. 23 x 2 = ________
12. 56 x 3 = ________
13. 36 x 5 = ________
14. 71 x 2 = ________
15. 21 x 4 = ________
16. 64 x 5 = ________
17. 47 x 3 = ________
18. 31 x 4 = ________
19. 69 x 2 = ________
20. 28 x 3 = ________
21. 82 x 5 = ________
22. 49 x 4 = ________
23. 36 x 2 = ________
24. 83 x 3 = ________
25. 27 x 5 = ________

Mental Math 19

1. $3 \times 6 =$ ________
2. $10 \times 6 =$ ________
3. $6 \times 6 =$ ________
4. $9 \times 6 =$ ________
5. $6 \times 8 =$ ________
6. $3 \times 4 =$ ________
7. $5 \times 6 =$ ________
8. $5 \times 4 =$ ________
9. $6 \times 7 =$ ________
10. $8 \times 4 =$ ________
11. $4 \times 6 =$ ________
12. $6 \times 0 =$ ________
13. $7 \times 3 =$ ________
14. $6 \times 9 =$ ________
15. $7 \times 6 =$ ________
16. $36 \div 6 =$ ________
17. $48 \div 6 =$ ________
18. $30 \div 5 =$ ________
19. $6 \div 6 =$ ________
20. $18 \div 6 =$ ________
21. $24 \div 6 =$ ________
22. $42 \div 6 =$ ________
23. $30 \div 6 =$ ________
24. $54 \div 6 =$ ________
25. $28 \div 4 =$ ________
26. $60 \div 6 =$ ________
27. $24 \div 6 =$ ________
28. $35 \div 5 =$ ________
29. $27 \div 3 =$ ________
30. $54 \div 6 =$ ________

Mental Math 20

1. 6 x 7 = ________
2. 9 x 7 = ________
3. 9 x 6 = ________
4. 7 x 8 = ________
5. 7 x 5 = ________
6. 8 x 7 = ________
7. 7 x 6 = ________
8. 4 x 7 = ________
9. 6 x 6 = ________
10. 5 x 7 = ________
11. 7 x 9 = ________
12. 6 x 8 = ________
13. 7 x 7 = ________
14. 49 x 7 = ________
15. 78 x 7 = ________
16. 56 ÷ 7 = ________
17. 42 ÷ 7 = ________
18. 48 ÷ 6 = ________
19. 49 ÷ 7 = ________
20. 28 ÷ 7 = ________
21. 14 ÷ 7 = ________
22. 7 ÷ 7 = ________
23. 21 ÷ 7 = ________
24. 35 ÷ 7 = ________
25. 42 ÷ 7 = ________
26. 42 ÷ 6 = ________
27. 54 ÷ 6 = ________
28. 35 ÷ 7 = ________
29. 63 ÷ 7 = ________
30. 49 ÷ 7 = ________

Mental Math 21

1. 9 x 8 = __________
2. 5 x 8 = __________
3. 8 x 8 = __________
4. 6 x 8 = __________
5. 8 x 5 = __________
6. 4 x 8 = __________
7. 7 x 8 = __________
8. 8 x 8 = __________
9. 7 x 6 = __________
10. 8 x 6 = __________
11. 8 x 7 = __________
12. 6 x 6 = __________
13. 7 x 7 = __________
14. 43 x 8 = __________
15. 82 x 8 = __________
16. 48 ÷ 8 = __________
17. 64 ÷ 8 = __________
18. 72 ÷ 8= __________
19. 40 ÷ 8 = __________
20. 49 ÷ 7 = __________
21. 32 ÷ 8 = __________
22. 36 ÷ 6 = __________
23. 63 ÷ 7 = __________
24. 64 ÷ 8 = __________
25. 56 ÷ 8 = __________
26. 48 ÷ 8 = __________
27. 48 ÷ 6 = __________
28. 24 ÷ 8 = __________
29. 56 ÷ 7 = __________
30. 16 ÷ 8 = __________

Mental Math 22

1. 6 x 9 = ________
2. 7 x 7 = ________
3. 9 x 9 = ________
4. 9 x 7 = ________
5. 8 x 8 = ________
6. 5 x 9 = ________
7. 8 x 9 = ________
8. 9 x 6 = ________
9. 7 x 9 = ________
10. 3 x 9 = ________
11. 4 x 9 = ________
12. 6 x 6 = ________
13. 9 x 8 = ________
14. 62 x 9 = ________
15. 21 x 9 = ________
16. 54 ÷ 9 = ________
17. 81 ÷ 9 = ________
18. 63 ÷ 9 = ________
19. 63 ÷ 7 = ________
20. 72 ÷ 9 = ________
21. 45 ÷ 9 = ________
22. 36 ÷ 6 = ________
23. 48 ÷ 8 = ________
24. 81 ÷ 9 = ________
25. 49 ÷ 7 = ________
26. 27 ÷ 9 = ________
27. 56 ÷ 8 = ________
28. 72 ÷ 8 = ________
29. 36 ÷ 9 = ________
30. 64 ÷ 8 = ________

Mental Math 23

1. 8 x 9 = __________
2. 48 ÷ 8 = __________
3. 45 ÷ 9 = __________
4. 9 x 7 = __________
5. 6 x 8 = __________
6. 81 ÷ 9 = __________
7. 6 x 7 = __________
8. 64 ÷ 8 = __________
9. 7 x 9 = __________
10. 9 x 8 = __________
11. 63 ÷ 7 = __________
12. 42 ÷ 6 = __________
13. 63 ÷ 9 = __________
14. 56 ÷ 7 = __________
15. 7 x 6 = __________
16. 42 ÷ 7 = __________
17. 72 ÷ 9 = __________
18. 36 ÷ 6 = __________
19. 54 ÷ 9 = __________
20. 56 ÷ 8 = __________
21. 9 x 9 = __________
22. 40 ÷ 8 = __________
23. 8 x 8 = __________
24. 7 x 7 = __________
25. 6 x 9 = __________
26. 72 ÷ 8 = __________
27. 7 x 8 = __________
28. 49 ÷ 7 = __________
29. 54 ÷ 6 = __________
30. 8 x 7 = __________

Mental Math 24

x	4			2		3		5
6			36					
7							56	
8		72						
9					63			

x	5	7	4	6	2	3	9	8
	40							
		49						
							81	
								48

x	2	7	3	6	4		9	8
				54				
7						35		
								64
		42						

Mental Math 25

1. 1000 – 652 = ________
2. 435 + 98 = ________
3. 81 ÷ 9 = ________
4. 4000 - 258 = ________
5. 6 x 8 = ________
6. 328 + 671 = ________
7. 3420 – 700 = ________
8. 64 ÷ 8 = ________
9. 52 x 4 = ________
10. 438 + 298 = ________
11. 800 x 7 = ________
12. 3256 – 96 = ________
13. 5200 – 432 = ________
14. 56 ÷ 7 = ________
15. 7 x 60 = ________
16. 3216 + 6541 = ________
17. 72 ÷ 9 = ________
18. 800 – 56 = ________
19. 54 + 45 = ________
20. 56 x 3 = ________
21. 90 x 9 = ________
22. 1363 + 80 = ________
23. 800 x 8 = ________
24. 4000 - 843 = ________
25. 6 x 90 = ________
26. 72 ÷ 8 = ________
27. 71 x 8 = ________
28. 3845 + 702 = ________
29. 1000 – 42 = ________
30. 500 x 7 = ________

This page is blank.

Exercise 8a

1. Add

3498 + 23	8671 + 346	3526 + 816
3690 + 546	1234 + 5178	6392 + 1843
2809 + 3862	7461 + 984	763 + 792

2. The sum of 594 and 3862 is ________________

3. The number that is 676 greater than 348 tens is ____________

4. (a) Using the digits 7, 1, 4, and 6 once; form the largest number.

   (b) Using the same digits once, form the smallest number

   (c) The sum of the two numbers you found is ______________

5. A plane traveled 4368 miles from Town A to Town B. It then flew another 3562 miles to Town C. How far away is Town C from Town A?

---

6. There are 2465 boys in a town. There are 78 more girls than boys.
(a) How many girls are there?

(b) How many children are there altogether?

---

7. A computer costs $1369 and a printer costs $819. John has $2000. Does he have enough money?

WE ARE ALL RELATED

A CELEBRATION OF OUR CULTURAL HERITAGE

Ashley Allen

Naveen Arneja

Derek Bulhoes

Pauline Chan

Eric Cho

Steven Chow

Wendy Chow

Lilian Chung

Robert Fox

Ifraaz Khan

Tho Anh Lam

Chad Lambert

Roderick Lee

Curtis Lew

Kevin Li

Richard Marshall

Cindy Mehat

David Parente

Ivan Pelzer

Ian Pham

Lucy Phan

Kaushal Reddy

Jeffery Shum

David Story

Alice Walkus

Christine White

Phillip Wong

Becca Yu

G.T. CUNNINGHAM ELEMENTARY SCHOOL, VANCOUVER BC

Canadian Cataloguing in Publication Data
We are all related: A Celebration of Our Cultural Heritage.

ISBN 0-9680479-0-4

Catalogue of an exhibition.
1. Children's art - British Columbia - Vancouver - Exhibitions. 2. Multiculturalism in art - Exhibitions. 3. Art, Modern - 20th century - British Columbia - Vancouver - Exhibitions. 4. Art, Canadian - British Columbia - Vancouver - Exhibitions. I. Allen, Ashley. II. Littlechild, George. III George T. Cunningham Elementary School (Vancouver, B.C.)
N362.2.C3W4 1996 704'.0544'097113307471133 C96-910026-4

PRODUCTION CREDITS

Designed by Ande Axelrod
Photography by James Jardine
Colour Separations by Hemlock Colour Scan

PUBLISHED BY

George T. Cunningham Elementary School
2330 East 37th Avenue
Vancouver, BC Canada V5R 2T3
Printed in Hong Kong

DISTRIBUTED BY

Polester Book Publishers
1011 Commercial Drive, Second Floor
Vancouver, BC Canada V5L 3X1 Tel: (604) 251-9718

ISLAND PAPER MILLS
DIVISION OF
E.B. EDDY FOREST PRODUCTS LTD.

Province of British Columbia
Multiculturalism BC

CIBC

VanCity

Hongkong Bank of Canada

VSB

ROYAL BANK
VICTORIA & 49TH
BRANCH

中僑互助會
S.U.C.C.E.S.S.

MOSAIC

Ande Axelrod
Graphic Design

Surrey Art Gallery
Exhibitions and Education in Contemporary Art since 1975

BUSINESS MART
Full Business Service Centre

POLESTAR
BOOK PUBLISHERS

IN DEDICATION

TO THE CREATIVE SPIRIT WITHIN US
THAT HAS THE POWER TO DRAW HUMANITY TOGETHER
AND CONNECT US TO THE VALUE OF
OUR NATURAL ENVIRONMENT.

◆

TO THE ELDERS FOR SHARING YOUR WISDOM
IN ORDER TO BETTER PREPARE US
FOR LIVING WITH DIGNITY, COURAGE AND COMPASSION.

◆

TO CHILDREN EVERYWHERE
FOR SHARING YOUR IMAGINATION AND CREATIVITY.

YOU GIVE US REASON TO REJOICE.

FOREWORD

I was delighted to learn of the "We Are All Related" project, even more so once I knew it would become a book. The artwork and words of the youth are important.

Sharole Brown and Alison Diesvelt saw a vision; a vision through art and words that tell stories of a cross-cultural group of students. These stories stem from Canadian youth of diverse backgrounds. These children's artworks and words tell stories about identity, culture and community.

Stories told through art are important, particularly these stories, as they can help break down stereotypes and allow us to become more understanding of other people. People from the First Nations, Indo-Canadian, Jewish, Asian, Ukrainian, Scandinavian, German, Welsh, English, Irish heritage - These are some of the many cultural groups in Canada today. And what about the bi-racial child?

I, as an artist, have used family history, photographs and cultural elements in my art to tell stories about history, social and political issues.

I believe our ancestors are very important, as without them, their culture and beliefs, we would not be here.

I, too, believe our elders are the keepers of knowledge and wisdom, and we should respect our elders.

And I believe our youth are our future. We must treat them well!

— Thank You,
George Littlechild, Plains Cree Artist

Oomana katapasinahaman kēqwa kayas achimoona, musinbīhoona equa nehēyow sēgigāowna intabutchitan kawētaman, tansi ooma kayas āgēpāsipimatsiah, āgipāsiwuskawēyah equa tansi agēsibimbīsiwa.

Gēspin āgīyawēyaoochi kātāuk memtoni namukēqwī kakskātānanō,
tansi āgēpāsibimatsia aboo tansi āgēsibāysimamtnātama. Ewksēsi āsitabookaytaman.

Mēna intapwātan, kātāuk ooki, āqwanāwātakik ēnēsewin equa āqwanāwātakik oomamtonāchigunawow.
Humm, gēchāmēkook kātāuk.

Ookik mēna Awasisuk qwāusk nakatōgatēkook, munachēhekook, āgoonik ookik Awasisuk ootā nēgān kamumsia.

— Hai Hai
George Littlechild, Plains Cree Artist

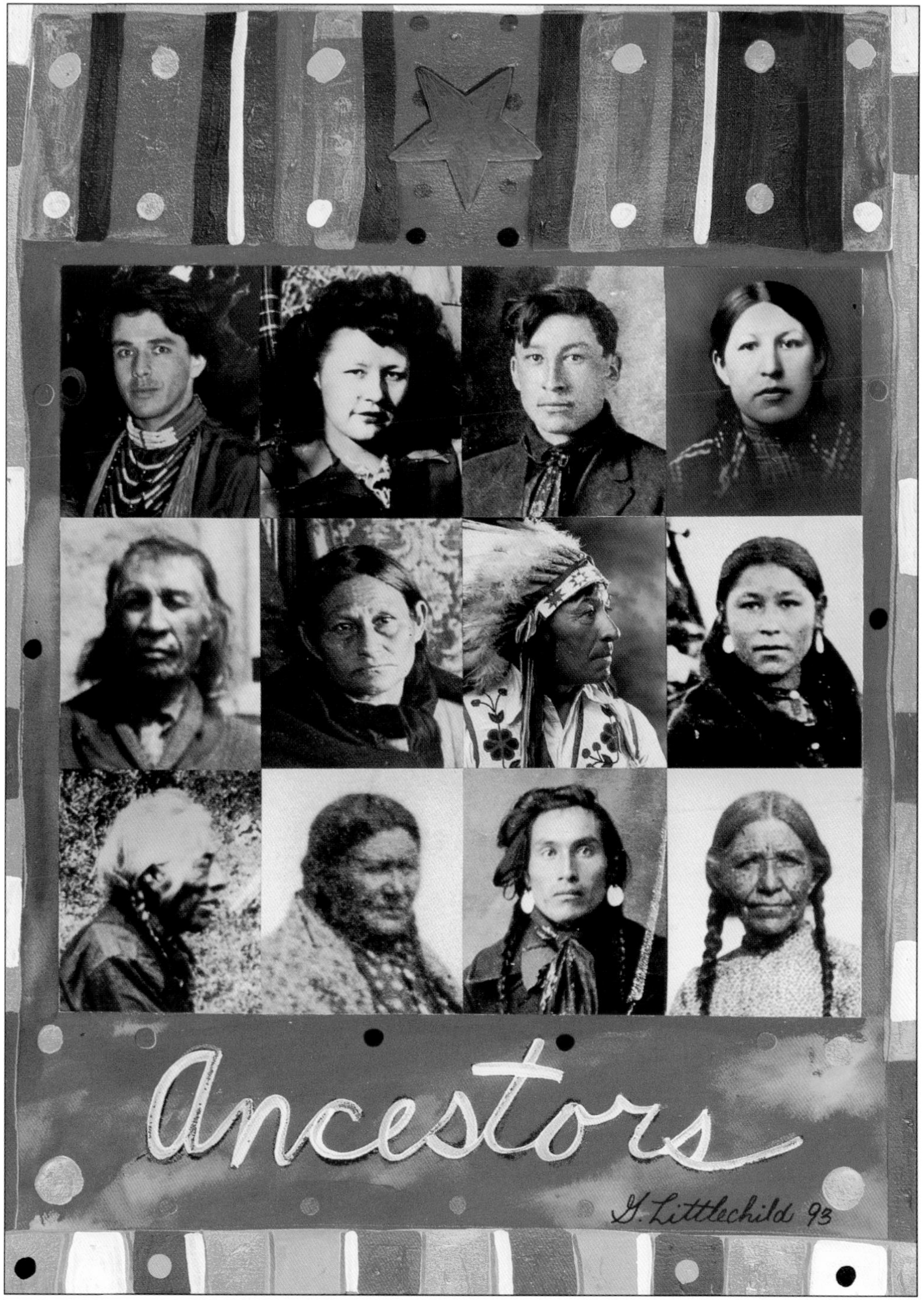

Ancestors, 1993
George Littlechild
mixed media, photo-collage on paper
collection of the artist.

Top Row, Left to Right
Me, my mother and my grandparents:

George Littlechild (1991)
Rachel Littlechild, my mother (1940's)
Edward Littlechild,
my grandfather (1915)
Bella Bull, my grandmother (1916)

Middle Row, Left to Right
My great-grandparents:

Alexander Littlechild,
my great-grandfather (1920's)
Jenny Cardinal,
my great-grandmother (1910)
Chief Francis Bull,
my great-grandfather (1930's)
Peggy Louis Natuasis,
my great-grandmother (1890's)

Bottom Row, Left to Right
My great-great-grandparents:

Chief Louis Bull,
my great-great-grandfather (1920's)
Marianne Sikak,
my great-great-grandmother (1905)
Louis Natuasis,
my great-great-grandfather (1898)
Betsy Samson,
my great-great-grandmother (1940's)

Dedication
For my ancestors: I thank you for surviving when so many did not. You make me proud of who I am because of who you were.

INTRODUCTION

We Are All Related is the work of 28 children, ranging in age from eight to twelve years old, from G.T. Cunningham Elementary School in Vancouver. It is the result of an "Artist-in-Residence" program initiated during the 1994/95 school year.

Visual art is a basic way children can learn to make sense of their society and their own place in it. The children whose art is featured in *We Are All Related* worked with photographs of their elders and themselves to explore and express ideas about their own history and heritage. Their creative and complex collages convey much more about themselves than could any written or spoken work.

For eight months, students were engaged in an inter-generational and inter-cultural project that eventually led to a touring Heritage Collage exhibition curated by the Surrey Art Gallery. Students were encouraged to talk and listen to the elders in their families and to visit elders in their school and larger community. Students were exposed to different cultures through this experience by sharing their own stories with one another. Role-playing, story-telling, reading and writing were all part of this inter-disciplinary project. Ellen Rothstein, teacher librarian, and Janet Dempsey, ESL resource teacher, prepared the students with background material.

There was an emphasis on First Nations culture through exposure to stories, legends, beliefs and ideas as revealed by First Nations teachers and elders. Geraldine Bob and Lorna Williams, First Nations education specialists (VSB) were important resources for the students, sharing their knowledge and experience. Chief Leonard George was an elder who also shared his stories and legends with the students. George Littlechild's work, *Ancestors,* 1993, is part of this exhibit. His paintings and collages were a great influence on the children's artwork. Students met with Littlechild for a tour of his show at the Tribal Art Gallery in Vancouver. They listened to his stories and learned about his family history.

Artist-in-residence Alison Diesvelt worked with students to develop the skills required to complete the works. She introduced students to various materials and techniques, including photography, hand-tinting, block printing, drawing and painting. The resulting mixed-media works on paper are personal and well-planned compositions. Text, written by the students, helps us to understand their work.

By spending some time with this exhibit we can learn something about the children and their cultural heritage. Beyond that, we can see the pride and self-esteem that this project has helped each student express. Students who find it difficult to communicate through writing or speaking, or students who are learning English, have been able to communicate effectively through a visual language. Working with an art specialist and looking at the work of contemporary artists has expanded their ideas about what Art is and what it can accomplish. They've learned about problem-solving, creativity, design and composition. This art-focused project and its results, including this show, are strong evidence supporting the idea that Art is an important and indispensible part of education and learning.

—Amir Alibhai, *Assistant Curator, Surrey Art Gallery*

During the course of the exhibition at the Richmond Art Gallery, it was a pleasure to see the excitement and enthusiasm this show gave to both the public viewers, and especially to the students who came to look and create their own "Heritage Collages".

To me, "We Are All Related" means we are all related and therefore worthy of respect. When I see the results of young artists sitting down with pictures of their families, elders and themselves, and spending time expressing their connection, I can't help think of how respectful that is, and how powerful art is as a tool to convey that message.

This show is not just about family, culture, or being "related", it is also about the power of art to transform the viewer. By presenting visual symbols of individual artists, charged with their personal meanings, viewers connect across cultures and generations and to their own stories. Our audience here has made that so abundantly clear with the stories they've shared with us upon seeing the show.

— Peter F. Harris, *Cultural Assistant, Richmond Art Gallery*

PREFACE

Visual symbols are a powerful and immediate connection to our cultural heritage. They are a reflection of cultural myths, legends, values and history. This is where "art finds its roots and inspiration".

As is stated by the Canadian Society for Education through Art, art is a part of the cultural heritage of every society. Art Education is a fundamental part of human growth and development. Through art education, children develop skills and confidence. They are sensitized to seeing similarities in differences and are more aware of the harmonious relationship of parts and wholes. Creative and personal self-expression through art facilitates deeper insight into culture and positive human growth.

We Are All Related is a true reflection of our school's diverse cultural community. Each student was put in the role of the expert/teacher as they shared their family photographs, history, cultural symbols and values. Together they learned to listen, be patient and respectful of one another. These are fundamental steps in the learning process towards developing sensitivity and human compassion. These are skills we need for Life.

We Are All Related was developed in partnership with our School Board's "Artist-in-Residence" program, coordinated by Peggy Bochun. In order to facilitate the students' aesthetic sensibilities and skills, it was important that they were able to see original art works as well as reproductions. Over several weeks, students witnessed and experienced the steps an artist might take in order to create an art work. They were encouraged to include personal symbols that related to their cultural heritage, as well as First Nations values and the natural environment. Individual pride and cultural empowerment grew as cultural diversity was embraced.

Alison Diesvelt's original art work as well as reproductions from artists of various cultures and styles (especially George Littlechild) facilitated enthusiastic lessons in Art History and Art Criticism. The students visited an art gallery and saw George Littlechild's latest original art works.

Students became aware of the circumstances in which artists' works were created. First Nations guests shared their values and forms of cultural expressions that inspired students to do the same. Students highlighted their cultural heritage and communicated it to others. Out of school excursions to Stanley Park and The Gallery of Tribal Art provided an opportunity to develop a new awareness of First Nations history, values and art. By interviewing their elders, students developed further knowledge and respect for their cultural heritage and themselves as individuals.

The *We Are All Related* programme was developed with the expertise of the First Nations Education Department of the Vancouver School Board. "All My Relations", a First Nations, Fine Arts based curriculum guide, and K. Garnier's "Our Elders Speak..." were inspirational resources.

We Are All Related was deliberately planned from its initial concept to be a means by which the diverse resources within our school and community could be tapped. G. T. Cunningham School staff and administrators greatly facilitated this project's success. Our principal, Suzanne Starr, provided invaluable support towards the final publication of this project. Volunteers shared their art, stories, games, and history of their cultural heritage. First Nations values of respecting ourselves, others (especially elders), and the environment, were shared by a Chief, an author, and a graduate student through their language, legends, music and family stories.. Elders, parents and family members played a crucial role. The children have written messages to be passed on. These have been translated into a language that relates to their cultural heritage.

The students learned about First Nations History, Culture and Art in a truly personal and meaningful way. This book is a celebration of art, culture and families. We hope it inspires people of all ages to create their own family heritage collage.

— On behalf of the G.T. Cunningham Artists and Authors
Sharole Brown, *Teacher, We are All Related Project Coordinator.*

I AM ASHLEY ALLEN

My family comes from the Ukraine and Ireland.
The elders in this collage are my mom and dad.
I drew pysanky easter eggs because they stand for my culture.
The border on my collage is a pattern of flowers, suns, fish and crosses. There is a photo of my mom with her grade four class. I am standing over my mom and her classmates. My mom and I are on the left. My dad and I are on the right.

I think this project was fun, good and interesting because it is about other cultures. We are all the same because we are human.

THE ELDERS SPEAK

"I would like young people to learn from me...to be patient, be polite and not be angry all the time. If you smile it makes you happy."

— Avon Allen (Ashley's grandma)

TO ME, "WE ARE ALL RELATED" MEANS FRIENDSHIP AND BEING NICE TOGETHER.
BE KIND EVERYDAY AND GIVE TO OTHERS.

◆

**Для мене "Ми всі споріднені" означає дружбу і бути всім приємними.
Бути добрими щодня та давати другим.**

I AM NAVEEN ARNEJA

My family comes from India.
The elders in my collage are my grandma, grandpa and dad.
The photograph of me shows me with my grandma when I was about three years old.
I drew a sky, fence and two religious dolls because they show strength.
The border on my collage is a pattern of four lines, triangles and fish.

I think this project was worthwhile because I learned more about my culture and family.

THE ELDERS SPEAK

"I would like young people to learn from me...to respect the family and not to go bad."

— Prem Arneja (Naveen's grandma)

TO ME, "WE ARE ALL RELATED" MEANS THAT WE ARE ALL CONNECTED.
ALTHOUGH WE ALL LOOK DIFFERENT WE ARE ALL HUMAN AND WE ARE ALL RELATED.
HOLD ON TO YOUR DREAM

◆

ਮੇਰੇ ਲਈ "ਅਸੀਂ ਸਭ ਸਬੰਧੀ ਹਾਂ" ਦਾ ਅਰਥ ਹੈ ਕਿ ਅਸੀਂ ਸਭ ਆਪਸ ਵਿਚ ਜੁੜੇ ਹੋਏ ਹਾਂ।
ਦੇਖਣ ਵਿਚ ਭਾਵੇਂ ਵੱਖਰੇ ਲਗਦੇ ਹਾਂ ਪਰ ਅਸੀਂ ਸਭ ਇਨਸਾਨ ਹਾਂ ਅਤੇ ਇਕ ਦੂਜੇ ਨਾਲ ਸਬੰਧਿਤ ਹਾਂ।

I AM DEREK BULHOES

My family comes from Portugal.
The elders in this collage are grandpa and grandma (my dad's mother and father).
The photograph shows me with my dad holding me. I was three years old. I drew a fishing boat from an encyclopedia picture on Portugal found in our school library. People in Portugal do a lot fishing. I like to fish too.
The border on my collage is a pattern of fish, a sun and a triangle.
I thought they looked nice together.

I think this project was fun and interesting. I learned about Portugal and the importance of respecting each other. Other people can learn about different cultures by looking at the heritage collages.

THE ELDERS SPEAK

"I would like young people to learn from me...to be helpful and not to be mean."

— Noberto Bulhoes (Derek's dad)

TO ME "WE ARE ALL RELATED" MEANS THAT WE ARE FRIENDS.
RESPECT ONE ANOTHER, BEHAVE AND PLAY SAFE.

◆

PARA MIM "SOMOS TODOS PARENTES" QUER DIZER QUE SOMOS AMIGOS.
RESPEITE UM AO OUTRO, COMPORTE-SE E TENHA CUIDADO.

I AM PAULINE CHAN

My family comes from Hong Kong.
The elders in this collage are mom and dad.
The photograph shows me when I was six years old. I write Chinese words because they stand for our culture. The Chinese words in my collage mean: sun, moon, mountain, red, girl, boy, grandma and grandpa.
The border on my collage is a pattern of suns, trees and geometric shapes.

I enjoyed this project because placing the photographs was fun.

THE ELDERS SPEAK

"I would like young people to learn from me...to listen to your elders and don't fight with your brother."

— Mei Va Kwan (Pauline's grandma)

TO ME "WE ARE ALL RELATED" MEANS THAT WE ARE ALL CONNECTED.
I LEARNED THAT WE SHOULD TRY TO HAVE BALANCE IN OUR LIVES AND RESPECT EACH OTHER.

◆

我覺得「本是同根生」意思是我們都可聯接起來。
我們都應該追求生活的均衡，並彼此尊重。

I AM ERIC PETER CHO

My family comes from China and Hong Kong.
The elders in this collage are my mom, Wai Fong and my dad, Li Cho.
The photograph shows me with my dad and mom.
In the left corner of the picture, is my mom with a purple collar. In the right corner are my mom and dad carrying me in Queen Elizabeth Park.
The border on my collage is a pattern of Chinese writing: sun, water, up and down. I drew a dragon and a tiger because they symbolize power, strength and Chinese culture. The Chinese writing means tiger and cat.

I think this project was important because it showed our feelings and how great our art came out.

THE ELDERS SPEAK

"I would like young people to learn from me...to find a job to do and not be bad."

— Lui An (Eric's grandpa)

Brooklyn Park Middle School
Media Center

TO ME "WE ARE ALL RELATED" MEANS THAT WE ARE ALL CONNECTED.
DO YOUR BEST AND BE HELPFUL TO EACH OTHER AND YOU WILL SUCCEED IN THE FUTURE.

◆

我解釋「本是同根生」的定義是：我們本來都有連繫。
凡事盡力而為，彼此幫助，必定成功在望。

I AM STEVEN SIU KURN CHOW

My family comes from China and the United Kingdom.
The elders in this collage are Son Lim Lam and Hoi Lim Lam.
The photograph shows me with my family in Squamish.
I drew a farm because my dad has one in Burnaby and my uncle has one in Delta.
The border on my collage is a pattern of sunsets, suns, stars and stripes.

I think this project was good because it helped me with symbols and patterns. I learned that strong values can make you have a more balanced and better life.

THE ELDERS SPEAK

"I would like young people to learn from me...to be good and not to be lazy."

— Son Lim Lam (Steven's grandma)

TO ME "WE ARE ALL RELATED" MEANS THAT WE ARE ALL CONNECTED.
WE SHOULD LIVE IN HARMONY.

◆

我認爲「本是同根生」即是大家息息相關。
我們應該在和諧中共處。

I AM WENDY CHOW

My family comes from China.
The elders in this collage are my mom and grandma.
The photograph shows me with my mom and grandma.
I drew a Chinese Temple because it stands for China. I put the flowers on the Chinese Temple because I like flowers. I picked the shapes because they mean nature.
The border on my collage is a pattern of geometric shapes, suns, moons and birds.

I think this project was super because it was outstanding and wonderful. I like this project because I got to draw and paint and handcolour the photographs.

THE ELDERS SPEAK

"We would like young people to learn from us...to help more often rather than be lazy and to read your books so you get smart."

— Ho Wai and Husiu (Wendy's grandma and mom)

TO ME,
"WE ARE ALL RELATED"
MEANS THAT
WE ARE ALL CONNECTED.

MY MESSAGE IS
TO RESPECT
THE ENVIRONMENT

◆

依我的看法，「本是同根生」表示我們大家根本是一脈相連的。我們應該愛護環境。

I AM LILIAN CHUNG

My family comes from China.
The elders in this collage are my grandpa (Fred Koo), my great-grandpa and great-grandma.
The photograph shows me standing with them.
I drew a lucky money envelope because it means good luck.
The border on my collage is a pattern of crosses, animals, moons, stars and lines.

I think this project was important because we are all connected.

THE ELDERS SPEAK

"I would like young people to learn from me...to share things, don't be mad and not to be slow or mean."

— Wong Koo (Lilian's grandma)

TO ME "WE ARE ALL RELATED" MEANS THAT WE ARE ALL A FAMILY.
ALL YOU NEED IS DETERMINATION AND EFFORT.

◆

對我來説，「本是同根生」可以解作我們同屬一個大家庭。
我們需要下定決心，努力向前。

I AM ROBERT FOX

I am a First Nations person. I am Northern Tutchone. My family comes from the Yukon Territory. The elder in this collage is my grandmother, Effie.
The photograph shows me with my grandmother.
I drew a yin-yang symbol on my shirt because it stands for black and white, good and bad.
The border on my collage is a pattern of trees and buildings. It shows the separation of Mother Nature and civilization. The inner border symbolizes the Wolf Clan and the Crow Clan. I come from the Crow Clan.

I think this project was very educational because it taught kids about Aboriginal people.

THE ELDERS SPEAK

"I would like young people to learn from me...to play sports, keep healthy and not to watch TV anymore."

— Gordon Brunton (Robert's grandpa)

TO ME "WE ARE ALL RELATED" MEANS THAT WE ARE RELATED BY FRIENDSHIP AND THE BOND BETWEEN US, BECAUSE WE ARE NOT ALL RELATED BY BLOOD. RESPECT YOURSELF AND THE ENVIRONMENT.

◆

DÄN K'Í TAYINTÄH YÉTS'ECH'I. EDEYE SÓTHÄN N'ÄNINDDHÄT JÄN NÄN KA.

I AM IFRAAZ KHAN

My family comes from Fiji.
The elder in this collage is a policeman standing outside the parliament building in Fiji which is close to my uncle's house. It shows me with my sister, Naidia, when I was three years old.
I drew mountains because they stand for my culture. Fiji has a lot of mountains.
The border on my collage is a pattern of lines, leaves and flowers.

I think this project was fantastic because I learned more about nations around the world.

THE ELDERS SPEAK

"I would like young people to learn from me...self discipline, to be nice and good and not to swear at people."

— Fatima Ali (Ifraaz's grandma)

TO ME "WE ARE ALL RELATED" MEANS THAT WE ARE ALL CONNECTED.
LEARN AND GET SMARTER.

◆

मेरे लिए "हम सब सम्बन्धी हैं "का अर्थ है कि हम सब आपस में जुड़े हुए हैं।
शिक्षा प्राप्त करो और समझदार बनो।

I AM THO ANH LAM

My family comes from Vietnam.
The elders in this collage are my mom and dad. The photograph in the lower right corner shows me with my family.
I drew a river because it represents my culture.
The border on my collage is a pattern of stars and the four elements.

I think this project was great because it was all about First Nations.

THE ELDERS SPEAK

"I would like young people to learn from me...to study hard in order to succeed in the future and not to waste time."

— Dung Lam (Tho's dad)

TO ME "WE ARE ALL RELATED" MEANS THAT WE ARE ALL CONNECTED.
DON'T BE GREEDY.

Đối với tôi "Chúng Ta Đều Có Liên Hệ" có nghĩa là chúng ta đều có liên quan với nhau.
Đừng nên tham lam.

I AM CHAD LAMBERT

My family comes from Edmonton. Some of my family members are Ojibway.
The elder in this collage is my aunt, Debra Nakinak.
The photograph shows me with Debra (Dee Dee).
I drew a medicine wheel because it shows a little of my culture.
The border on my collage is a pattern of food, claws and eggs.

I think this project was interesting because it taught me a lot of things, about art, heritage and culture.

THE ELDERS SPEAK

"I would like young people to learn from me...to be your own self, don't follow others and not to be a follower and do things you know you should not do."

— Debra Nakinak (Chad's aunt)

TO ME "WE ARE ALL RELATED" MEANS IT DOESN'T MATTER WHAT COLOUR WE ARE; WE ARE ALL HUMAN.
YOU SHOULD ALWAYS BE YOURSELF.

◆

NA SAUB, TA BID DA GA GWAE EH ZHI BI MA DIZ ZIN

I AM RODERICK KARL LEE

My family comes from China.
The elders in this collage are my mom, dad and my grandma.
The photograph shows me beside my grandma and above my mom and dad who are on the rock.
I drew a dragon because it means a boy, and a phoenix because it stands for a girl.
The border on my collage is a pattern of an eagle and the four elements.

I learned about art and how important it is to respect myself, other people and Mother Earth.

THE ELDERS SPEAK

"I would like young people to learn from me... to get a good education and not to smoke."

— Larry Lee (Roderick's dad)

TO ME
"WE ARE ALL RELATED"
MEANS THAT
EVERYTHING ON EARTH
HAS A PURPOSE.

ALL THAT IS NEEDED
IS DETERMINATION
AND EFFORT
AND SURELY IT CAN BE
ACCOMPLISHED.

◆

對我來說，「本是同根生」的意思是世界上每樣事物都有個目的。
靠著決心和毅力，這些目的都可以達成。

I AM CURTIS SUI CHANG LEW

My family comes from China.
The elders in this collage are my grandma and grandpa.
The photograph above shows me holding a family picture. The photograph below shows me between my brother and grandma at a wedding reception.
I drew two dragons because they stand for strength.
The border on my collage is a pattern of geometric shapes and animals. The writing on the two drums is my Chinese name.

I think this project was fun because I liked to draw and paint.

THE ELDERS SPEAK

I would like young people to learn from me...to draw and not to smoke.

— Wen Fong Lew (Curtis' grandfather)

TO ME "WE ARE ALL RELATED" MEANS THAT WE ARE ALL SIMILAR IN DIFFERENCES.
WE ARE ALL RELATED BECAUSE WE ARE LIVING THINGS.

◆

「本是同根生」等於我們在差異中有共通之點。
我們都是有生命的東西，因此有密切的關係。

I AM KEVIN J.B. LI

My family comes from China.
The elder in this collage is my grandfather.
The photograph shows me with my grandfather when I was three or four years old.
I drew a dragon because it means Spring and new life.
The border on my collage is a pattern of trees and stars.

I think this project was exciting because it was fun drawing, painting and gluing.
I learned that we should respect one another, help others and think about others.

THE ELDERS SPEAK

"I would like young people to learn from me...to be good students and not to be bad students."

— Huo Luo (Kevin's grandfather)

TO ME "WE ARE ALL RELATED" MEANS THAT WE ARE ALWAYS CONNECTED.
EVERYBODY IS THE SAME AS YOU.

◆

「本是同根生」等於我們彼此都有關係。
人人和你都是一樣。

I AM RICHIE YUREVICH MIHAILO CURTIS MARSHALL

My family comes from the Ukraine and Germany.
The elders in this collage are my aunties, great-grandma, great-great-grandma and my dad.
The baby in the centre of this collage is my dad.
The photograph of the other baby is me.
I drew Ukrainian eggs because they symbolize my culture.
The border on my collage is a pattern of gems and suns.

I think this project was excellent and fun because it showed how First Nations people live, and the meaning of their symbols.

THE ELDERS SPEAK

"I would like young people to learn from me...to be more responsible (not to lose things), to bake homemade food and not to waste money, cook better, buy in bulk, not fast foods."

— Maria Zotzman (Richard's grandma)

TO ME "WE ARE ALL RELATED" MEANS THAT WE ARE ALL CONNECTED.
PURPOSE, PASSION, SERVICE, WITH THESE YOU WILL HAVE A MORE BALANCED LIFE.

◆

Для мене "Ми всі споріднені" означає що ми всі зв'язани друг з другом.
Цілеспрямованість, запал, допомога: з цим життя буде більш рівноважним.

I AM CINDY MEHAT

My family comes from India.
The elders in this collage are my mommy, Sharnjit and dad, Raminder Mehat.
I drew a line of dogs because they often help people in India. I had five dogs, when I stayed there.
My mommy is wearing a punjabi suit and the colours on her suit are dark pink, and black with golden diamonds. My daddy is wearing a man's suit and a tie. The suit is black and the tie is dark red and grey with a pattern.
The border on my collage is a pattern of suns, stars, boxes and lines.

I think this project was excellent and fun because it taught me all about First Nations symbols. It is important to learn about different beliefs and different cultural symbols. By becoming more aware of these we can see that people have similar values and beliefs.

THE ELDERS SPEAK

"I would like young people to learn from me...to respect others and not to smoke."

— Raminder Mehat (Cindy's daddy)

TO ME "WE ARE ALL RELATED" MEANS THAT WE ARE ALL CONNECTED.
LIVE IN PEACE.

◆

ਮੇਰੇ ਲਈ "ਅਸੀਂ ਸਭ ਸਬੰਧੀ ਹਾਂ" ਦਾ ਅਰਥ ਹੈ ਕਿ ਅਸੀਂ ਸਭ ਆਪਸ ਵਿਚ ਜੁੜੇ ਹੋਏ ਹਾਂ।
ਸ਼ਾਂਤੀ ਨਾਲ ਰਹੋ ।

I AM DAVID PARENTE

My family comes from Italy.
The elders in this collage are my mom, grandma and grandpa.
The photograph shows me with my mom and brother.
I drew a temple and snakes because they stand for Rome, Italy.
The border on my collage is a pattern of potato prints that symbolize stars.

I think this project was neat because the project made me feel good.

THE ELDERS SPEAK

"I would like young people to learn from me...to make their bed and not to talk back to others."

— Ledina Dinofrio (David's grandma)

TO ME "WE ARE ALL RELATED" MEANS THAT WE ARE ALL CONNECTED.
DON'T BE BAD AND DON'T BE A RACIST.

◆

PER ME, SIAMO TUTTI UNA GRANDE FAMIGLIA: CIÒ SIGNIFICA CHE TUTTI ABBIAMO QUALCOSA IN COMUNE.
NON ESSERE MALVAGIO. NON ESSERE RAZZISTA.

I AM OSCAR IVAN PELZER

My family comes from Canada and Mexico.
The elders in this collage are Aggie and Rudy.
The photograph in the lower left shows me with my dad in Hawaii. The little picture shows my brother, Fernando, and I when we were adopted. There are Mexican pesos in the picture.
I drew a Mexican flag in the picture because it shows my culture.
The border on my collage is a pattern of rectangles and stripes.

I think this project was wonderful because we got to draw about our family.

THE ELDERS SPEAK

"I would like young people to learn from me...to have good manners and not to lie."

— Sybil Christianson (Ivan's grandma)

TO ME "WE ARE ARE RELATED" MEANS THAT WE ARE ALL CONNECTED.
NEVER TO GIVE UP WHEN THINGS ARE HARD.

◆

"TODOS ESTAMOS RELACIONADOS", PARA MÍ SIGNIFICA QUE ESTAMOS CONECTADOS.
JAMAS DARNOS POR VENCIDOS EN TIEMPOS DIFÍCILES.

I AM IAN HIEN GIA TUTI PHAM

My family comes from Vietnam.
The elders in this collage are my grandma, Xuyen Tran and my grandpa.
The photograph shows me holding a picture of my grandma and grandpa when they were young.
I drew a dragon and phoenix because they stand for a strong marriage.
The border on my collage is a pattern of geometric shapes, an eagle and a fish. I drew the eagle because it is an important symbol of the First Nations people.
It symbolizes strength and good eyesight.

I think this project was excellent because it helped me respect the elders.

THE ELDERS SPEAK

"I would like young people to learn from me...to eat your vegetables and not to lie."

— Xuyen Tran (Ian's grandma)

TO ME "WE ARE ALL RELATED" MEANS THAT WE ARE ALL IN THE CIRCLE OF LIFE.
WE SHOULD ALL LIVE IN HARMONY.

◆

Đối với tôi "Chúng Ta Đều Có Liên Hệ" có nghĩa là chúng ta đều ở trong quỹ đạo cuộc đời.
Chúng ta nên sống hòa thuận với nhau.

I AM LUCY PHAN

My family comes from China and Vietnam.
The elders in this collage are my grandpa and grandma, who are with me when I was three years old.
The photograph in the middle shows me holding this picture.
I drew two birds, hearts and a nest because my mom told me that our family likes them.
The border on my collage is a pattern of flowers and four lines. The lines stand for the four elements, which are air, fire (sun), water and earth.

I think this project was fun and interesting. It was important because I learned a lot about First Nations people and to respect one another.

THE ELDERS SPEAK

"I would like young people to learn from me...to be nice with your friends and not to be mean."

— Ngo Tich (Lucy's grandma)

TO ME "WE ARE ALL RELATED" MEANS THAT WE NEED TO RESPECT AND BE KIND TO EACH OTHER BECAUSE WE ARE ALL PEOPLE

TAKE IT EASY. DONT' BE SCARED IF YOU DON'T KNOW WHAT TO DO, JUST ASK AN ELDER, TEACHER OR FRIEND.

◆

「本是同根生」可以解作我們既然都是人，就要彼此尊重及寬待。
三思而行，有不懂得的地方，不要畏縮，應馬上請教師長或朋友。

I AM KAUSHAL REDDY

My family comes from the Fiji Islands.
The elders in this collage are my grandma, Saras Wati Raman and grandpa, Paras Raman.
The photograph with the elephant shows my grandparents when they went to India.
The photograph of the lady wearing the flowers is my mom getting married. The photograph with the goats shows my dad when he was on the farm.
I drew a goat because it stands for my horoscope sign.
The border on my collage is a pattern of geometric shapes, stars and four lines which represent the four elements.

I think this project was fantastic because I learned more about other people's cultures.

THE ELDERS SPEAK

"I would like young people to learn from me...to learn to like everyone and share and not to be bad."

— Saras Wati Raman (Kaushal's grandmother)

TO ME "WE ARE ALL RELATED" MEANS THAT WE ARE ALL CONNECTED.
RESPECT OTHERS, YOURSELF AND MOTHER EARTH.

◆

मेरे लिए "हम सब सम्बन्धी हैं "का अर्थ है कि हम सब आपस में जुड़े हुए हैं।
अपना, दूसरों का और धरती माता का आदर करो।

I AM JEFFERY WHAI YEEN SHUM

My family comes from Canton, China.
The elders in this collage are my mom, grandma, grandfather, auntie and uncle.
The photograph shows me with my mom and my dad, who is holding my sister.
I drew a dragon because it represents strength for my family.
The border on my collage is a pattern of geometric shapes and eagles. I put eagles on my border because they look neat and stand for power.

I think this project was fun to do because I've never done these things before. I also learned to respect other cultures and Mother Nature. If we respect other cultures and Mother Nature it would make a better life.

THE ELDERS SPEAK

"I would like young people to learn from me...to know more words and not to be lazy and impolite."

— P.E. Chow (Jeffrey's grandpa)

TO ME "WE ARE ALL RELATED" MEANS THAT WE ARE ALL CONNECTED. DON'T BE RACIST AND "WALK THE TALK" (DO WHAT YOU SAY YOU WILL DO).

「本是同根生」等於我們大家都可以連結起關係。
排除種族偏見，坐言起行（說得出，做得到）。

I AM DAVID STORY

My family comes from Canada.
The elder in this collage is my mom, Donna Story.
The photograph shows me with my brother, Daniel and my mom.
I drew a Canadian flag because it stands for Canada.
The border on my collage is a pattern of the four seasons.

I think this project *We Are All Related* was interesting because it shows different patterns, colours, and symbols. I learned to respect First Nations beliefs, Mother Nature and the importance of respecting myself.

THE ELDERS SPEAK

"I would like young people to learn from me...to be considerate of others."

— Donna Story (David's mom)

TO ME "WE ARE ALL RELATED" MEANS WE ARE ALL HUMAN AND WE ARE ALL EQUAL. RESPECT THE EARTH AND THE ANIMALS. TREAT THE EARTH AS YOU TREAT YOURSELF (WITH RESPECT).

◆

POUR MOI, «NOUS SOMMES TOUS APPARENTÉS» SIGNIFIE QU'EN TANT QU'ÊTRES HUMAINS, NOUS SOMMES TOUS ÉGAUX. RESPECTE LA TERRE ET LES ANIMAUX. TRAITE LA TERRE COMME TOI-MÊME (AVEC RESPECT).

I AM ALICE WALKUS

My family comes from Port Hardy, B.C. I am of the Kwakiutl Nation.
The elders in this collage are my grandpa and grandma.
The photograph shows me with my grandpa and grandma when I was about four years old.
I drew a Native dancer because it stands for our Native dancing.
The border on my collage is a pattern of Native designs.

I think this project was fun because I liked the things we had to use.

THE ELDERS SPEAK

"I would like young people to learn from me...my language and not to steal."

— Edith Walkus (Alice's mom)

TO ME "WE ARE ALL RELATED" MEANS EVERYBODY'S THE SAME.
WOULD YOU LIKE TO BE IN MY DANCE CLUB?

◆

LAXAN NOKE', 'WI'LAMEGANS DŁIDŁADŁOLA, HE'MANS LAGIŁ
'NAMUXW'AM BAGWANAMI.
K'IS S 'NIX KAS GAXA'OS GI'KA GAXANU'XW YAXWEGANU'XW.

I AM CHRISTINE WHITE

My family comes from the Philipines and Vancouver.
The elders in this collage are my two grandmothers, Eva and Adela, and my grandfather.
The photograph shows me when I was four years old, talking to my grandmother, Eva.
I drew a picture of a chain because it stands for peace, justice, and friendship.
The border on my collage is a pattern of evergreen trees and stripes.

I think this project was outstanding because it was exciting being able to go to the gallery to see George Littlechild.

THE ELDERS SPEAK

"I would like young people to learn from me... to learn how to behave and not to disobey their parents."

— Rose White (Christine's mom)

TO ME "WE ARE ALL RELATED" MEANS THAT WE HAVE TO TAKE CARE OF THE ANIMALS.
WE ALL HAVE TO TAKE CARE, DON'T BE GREEDY AND BE NICE TO OTHER PEOPLE.

◆

PARA SA AKIN "LAHAT TAYO AY MAGKAKAUGNAY" AY NANGANGAHULUGAN
NA KAILANGAN NATING ALAGAAN ANG MGA HAYOP.
LAHAT TAYO AY DAPAT NA MAGING MAINGAT. HUWAG MAGING SAKIM AT MAGING MABUTI SA PAKIKITUNGO SA KAPWA.

I AM PHILLIP WONG

My family comes from China.
The elders in this collage are my mom, aunt, uncle and grandfather.
The photograph shows me to the left of a big purple horse.
I drew a horse because it represents my mother's sign in Chinese astrology.
The border on my collage is a pattern of geometric shapes and fish.

I think this project was interesting because there was a focus on nature and families.

THE ELDERS SPEAK

"I would like young people to learn from me...English and exercise and not to play games."

— Chung Kwok Wong (Phillip's dad)

TO ME "WE ARE ALL RELATED" MEANS THAT WE ARE ALL CONNECTED..
DON'T BE GREEDY AND BE BALANCED.

◆

「本是同根生」表示我們的關係很密切。
不要作過份的妄想，應保持平衡。

I AM BECCA YU

My family comes from China.
The elders in this collage are my grandmothers and my grandpa.
The photograph shows me with my aunt, mom and grandma. The group of people in my collage are a few of my family members.
I drew the mountain of China because it stands for the dragons.
I drew that rabbit because I love animals.
The border on my collage is a pattern of stripes, trees and fire.

I think this project was a great idea because you can learn to respect all cultures.

THE ELDERS SPEAK

"I would like young people to learn from me... how to cook and not to turn bad. Don't spend too much money."

— Yan See Mui (Becca's grandma)

ACKNOWLEDGEMENTS

This project and publication was made possible through the co-sponsoring of MOSAIC and the generous support of the following groups.

MAJOR SPONSORS:

Province of BC Multicultural Grant Program
Island Paper Mills
Hemlock Printers Ltd.

SPONSORS:

CIBC & CIBC Aboriginal Banking
Hong Kong Bank of Canada
VanCity Credit Union
Royal Bank of Canada
Vancouver School Board:
Artist-in-Residence Program, *Peggy Bochun*
Multicultural and Anti-Racism Education Program, *Loma Wing*
First Nations Education, *Lorna Williams*
Sunrise Area Office, Associate Superintendent, *Eric Thomas*
ESL District Office - District Principal, *Hugh Hooper*
Curriculum Management - District Principal, *Val Overgaard*
The Ed May Social Responsibility Fund, *BCTF*
University of British Columbia Multicultural Education Department, *Dr. Kogila Adam-Moodley, David Lam Chair*

Special Thanks to all the elders and family members, past and present who participated in this project. *To GT Cunningham Elementary* - Staff and Administration for their enthusiastic support and encouragement. *To the talented GT Cunningham Choir,* led by Mr. Fenger, who performed at an exhibition reception in Richmond. *To George Littlechild* - whose art and books and generous spirit are a true inspiration to both students and teachers. *To Alison Diesvelt* - who as artist-in-residence taught us about design, composition and caring for one another. *To Amir Ali Alibhai* - who curated the inspired travelling exhibition of "We Are All Related". *To Geraldine Bob* - Our First Nations Education Resource Teacher who taught us about First Nations values, beliefs, friendship and the importance of respecting Mother Earth and having balance in your life. *To Lorna Williams* - A First Nations Education specialist and author who shared warmth, humor and wisdom through family stories, language and legends. *To Chief Leonard George* - who taught us lessons and inspired us with his family stories, First Nations legends and music. *To Donna Paskemin* - UBC Graduate student who kindly shared her Cree language and music. *To Nancy Blain* - coordinator for "Volunteers For Kids". *To Becky and Joseph Wong* - our senior volunteers. *To Francesca Lund* - for her budget advice. *To Ande Axelrod* - our patient, flexible book designer who shared her knowledge and skill to ensure this publication's success. *To Jim Jardine* - our art photographer whose understanding and expertise is greatly appreciated. *To Liane Davison* - curator at the Surrey Art Gallery, *Sue Teahan and Janice Douglas,* at the Vancouver Public Library, *Walter Stasiuk, Melanie Moore, Valerie and Dunham Craig* who have given generous encouragement. *T Peter Harris, Page-Hope Smith, Jane Wheeler* - at the Richmond Cultural Centre, *Anne Roberts* - VSB Trustee, *Gabriele Ailey,* UBC Art Education, *Noel Herron,* Cunningham Principal (now retired) *Charlie Naylor*, BCTF, *Sue Newell,* VanCity manager who have shown continued support towards intercultural and intergenera tional art projects. *To Hemlock Printers and Business Mart* - for their generosity in the production of this book. *To SUCCESS, MOSAIC, Vancouver Council for the Arts, BC Council for the Family, BC Teachers Federation, CBC French Radio* for their help in publici of this project.

Our heartfelt thanks and appreciation to all of the following people who helped provide translations: Plains Cree, *Wally Awasis,* Northern Tutchone, *Grace Wheeler and Eva Billy, Yukon College,* Kwakwaka'wakw/Kwak'wala, *Richard W. Dawson and Lorraine Hunt, Umista Cultural Centre, Alert Bay,* Ojibway, *Patricic Teichert,* Cantonese, *Anthony Chung,* Cantonese typesetting, *SUCCESS,* Vietnamese, *Huong Gia, Chuong Thi Pham and Xuyuei Tran,* Hindi, Punjabi, *Viren Joshi,* Italian, *Peter and Egidia Parente* French, *Tamar Kafka,* Portuguese, *Odette Bulhoes,* Ukrainian, Spanish, Tagalog, *MOSAIC.*

TO ME "WE ARE ALL RELATED" MEANS THAT EVERYONE IN THE WORLD IS CONNECTED..
I WANT PEOPLE TO WORK IN HARMONY AND TEAMWORK.

◆

我認爲「本是同根生」等於世界大同。
我覺得人類應該和諧共處，群策群力。